HALL GENERATORS
AND MAGNETORESISTORS
H.H.Wieder

Applied physics series

Series editor H.J.Goldsmid

HALL GENERATORS AND MAGNETORESISTORS
H.H.Wieder

Pion Limited, 207 Brondesbury Park, London NW2 5JN

Library edition   SBN 85086 019 9
Student edition   SBN 85086 020 2

Set on IBM 72 Composers by Pion Limited, London.
Printed in Great Britain by J.W.Arrowsmith Limited, Bristol.

Foreword

This monograph is intended for the practicing engineer or applied physicist in need of concise information on the wide range of laboratory and industrial applications of Hall generators and magnetoresistors. It is also intended for the engineering or physics student who has mastered the fundamental concepts of semiconductor devices or solid-state electronics. The treatment is conceptual rather than mathematical, with emphasis on the applications of such devices for the measurement and control of magnetic fields, for converting rectilinear or angular mechanical displacements of an object from a reference into proportional electrical signals, for high-speed multiplication of two electrical input variables, and for the implementation of corollary analog computer functions by the crossed-field interactions inherent in Hall effect and magnetoresistance phenomena.

For supplementary reading about the technology and uses of Hall generators and magnetoresistors, the reader is referred to the comprehensive monograph of H. Weiss, *Structure and Application of Galvanomagnetic Devices* (Pergamon Press, Oxford, 1969), and to the book by F. Kuhrt and H. J. Lippmann, *Hall-generatoren, Eigenschaften und Anwendungen* (Springer-Verlag, Berlin, 1968). For additional information on the theoretical foundations of galvanomagnetic phenomena and charge carrier transport in semiconductors of significance for the design and construction of Hall generators, the reader is referred to the monograph of E. H. Putley, *The Hall Effect and Related Phenomena* (Butterworths, London, 1960) and to the book by A. C. Beer, *Galvanomagnetic Effects in Semiconductors* (Academic Press, New York, 1963).

I wish to express my gratitude and appreciation to the cited authors and their publishers for permission to reproduce the illustrations whose origins are acknowledged throughout this book; to J. Dibrell for his active interest and support of research on galvanomagnetic phenomena and devices; to my colleague Dr. Derek Lile for his painstaking reading of the manuscript, and to my associates D. Collins, A. Clawson, and N. Davis. My special thanks go to Professor H. J. Goldsmid for his wise counsel and his valuable comments.

H.H.Wieder
Naval Electronics Laboratory Center,
San Diego, California

Acknowledgements

The author wishes to express his gratitude for the permissions received to reproduce the following material:

Barlow, H. E. M., Stephenson, L. M., 1959, *Proceedings of the Institution of Electrical Engineers, London,* **106B**, 27. Figure 1a.

von Borcke, V., Martens, H., Weiss, H., 1965, *Solid-state Electronics,* **8**, 365. Figure 2.

Davidson, R. S., Gourlay, R. D., 1966, *Solid-state Electronics,* **9**, 471. Figure 3.

Donaldson, G. W., 1966, *Solid-state Electronics,* **9**, 541. Figures 3 and 6. 1963, *Electronic Engineering,* **35**, 286. Figure 2.

Gallagher, R. C., Corak, W. S., 1966, *Solid-state Electronics,* **9**, 571. Figures 1 and 6.

Greiner, R. A., 1961, *Electronics,* August 25, page 52. Figures 2 and 4.

Haeusler, J., 1968, *Solid-state Electronics,* **11**, 173. Figures 5 and 6.

Hilsum, C., Rose-Innes, A. C., 1958, *Nature,* **182**, 1082. Figure 1.

Lippmann, H. J., Kuhrt, F., 1958, *Zeitschrift für Naturforschung,* **13a**, 474. Figure 12.

Lofgren, L., 1958, *Journal of Applied Physics,* **29**, 158. Figure 2.

Milnes, A. G., Weber, E. V., 1959, *Proceedings of the 1959 Electronic Component Conference, Philadelphia, Pennsylvania,* p.204. Figures 3 and 5.

Nalecz, M., 1961, *Bulletin de l'Academie Polonaise de Sciences,* **9**, 469. Figures 3, 4, and 5.

1966, *Solid-state Electronics,* **9**, 485. Figure 3.

Owston, C. N., 1967, *Journal of Scientific Instruments,* **44**, 798. Figure 1.

Strutt, U. J. O., 1959, *Electronic and Radio Engineer,* **36**, 2. Figure 9.

Honeywell Inc., California, 1968, EDN Magazine, **13**, November 11, page 87. Figure 1.

Product Sheet ISSI.

Beer, A. C., 1963, *Galvanomagnetic Effects in Semiconductors* (copyright Academic Press, New York). Figure 4.

Weiss, H., 1969, *Structure and Application of Galvanomagnetic Devices* (copyright Pergamon Press Ltd., Oxford). Figures 32.1 and 56.16.

Contents

Introduction

Electrons and holes, in metals and semiconductors, may be regarded as electrically charged particles subject to Newtonian mechanics while drifting in the direction of an electric field $\bar{E}$, with a velocity $\bar{v}$. All the electrons, assumed to have the same kinetic energy, are characterized by their charge $-e$, their effective mass m^*, and an acceleration $d^2\bar{v}/dt^2$ imparted by the force $\bar{F}_e = -e\bar{E}$. A magnetic induction $\bar{B}$ acting upon the drifting electrons brings into play the Lorentz force $\bar{F}_m = -e(v \times \bar{B})$ and the combination of electric and magnetically-induced forces

$$\bar{F} = -e(\bar{E} + \bar{v} \times \bar{B}) \tag{1.1}$$

acting on the electrons produces the two complementary galvanomagnetic phenomena, the Hall effect and the transverse magnetoresistance. In a rectangular plate, such as shown in Figure 1.1, the Lorentz force deflects the electrons in a direction orthogonal to both the electric and magnetic vectors, and the Hall field E_y, which arises in consequence, compensates the y component of the force $\bar{F}$. Defining the electron mobility $\mu = -e\bar{v}/\bar{F}$, the components of the velocity vector $\bar{v}$ in the steady state, are

$$v_x = \mu(E_x - v_y B)$$
$$v_y = \mu(E_y + v_x B)$$
$$v_z = \mu E_z = 0 . \tag{1.2}$$

Ohm's law, $\bar{J} = \sigma\bar{E}$, defines the linear relationship [1] between $\bar{E}$ and the current density vector $\bar{J} = ne\bar{v}$ in terms of the volume density of electrons n, crossing a unit surface area which is perpendicular to their velocity vector $\bar{v}$. The components of $\bar{J}$ are

$$J_x = nev_x = \sigma\left(\frac{E_x - \mu BE_y}{1 + \mu^2 B^2}\right)$$
$$J_y = nev_y = \sigma\left(\frac{E_y + \mu BE_x}{1 + \mu^2 B^2}\right) . \tag{1.3}$$

If a homogeneous, isotropic, rectangular Hall plate, such as that shown in Figure 1.1, with the Hall output terminals not connected to a load, is characterized by the scalar conductivity $\sigma = ne\mu$, then for $J_y = 0$

$$-E_y = \mu BE_x$$
$$v_x = \mu E_x . \tag{1.4}$$

Introducing Ohm's law into Equation (1.4) and solving for E_y leads to

$$E_y = -\frac{\mu}{\sigma}J_x B = -\frac{1}{ne}J_x B = -R_h J_x B . \tag{1.5}$$

The Hall coefficient R_h is negative for electrons and it is positive for holes (e is positive). It may be considered to be a constant of proportionality between the product $J_x B$ and the resultant Hall field E_y. If the input current i flowing through the Hall plate is expressed as $i = J_x wd$ and E_y is integrated over the width of the plate, then the Hall voltage v_h is

$$v_h = \int_0^w E_y \, dy = -R_h \left(\frac{iB}{d} \right). \tag{1.6}$$

It can be measured across the Hall output terminals, 3 and 4 of Figure 1.1. The proportionality between v_h and the product of the two

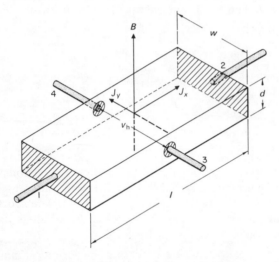

Figure 1.1. Schematic representation of a Hall plate. Magnetic induction B is along the z coordinate axis; input current density J_x and Hall current density J_y are along x and y axes respectively; shaded areas are electrodes.

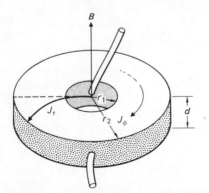

Figure 1.2. Cylindrical semiconductor Corbino disc with coaxial electrodes, thickness d, radial current density J_r, circumferential Hall current J_ϕ, and transverse magnetic induction B (Corbino, O. M., 1911, *Nuovo Cim.*, **1**, 397).

input variables i and B is of significance for a wide range of applications
described in this monograph.

In contrast with four-terminal Hall effect transducers, magnetoresistors
are two-terminal magnetically-variable resistors. The magnetoresistance
effect in a homogeneous isotropic material, with electrons as charge
carriers, is due either to a complete or to a partial short circuit of E_y.
A complete (galvanic) short circuit is shown, for example, in Figure 1.2.
The coaxial electrodes constrain E_y to zero and the transverse magnetic
induction produces a circumferential current in the disc.

From Equation (1.3), if $E_y = 0$[(1)], the magnetic field-dependent
resistivity $\rho(B) = E_x/J_x$ and the Hall current J_y are, respectively,

$$\rho(B) = \rho(0)(1 + \mu^2 B^2)$$
$$J_y \quad = \mu B J_x \tag{1.7}$$

where the scalar resistivity $\rho(0) = \sigma^{-1}$ and the magnetoresistance
$\Delta\rho/\rho_0 = \rho(B)/\rho(0) - 1$ is[(2)]

$$\frac{\Delta\rho}{\rho_0} = \mu^2 B^2 \ . \tag{1.8}$$

The Hall effect and magnetoresistance are complementary galvanomagnetic
phenomena. A partial short circuit of E_y, which allows a fractional Hall
current to flow in a Hall plate, introduces a magnetoresistance which alters
the linear v_h versus B dependence. Conversely, an incomplete short
circuit of E_y reduces the effective $\Delta\rho/\rho_0$ for a given B and alters its
quadratic dependence on B expressed in Equation (1.8).

1.1 Elementary design considerations
Emphasis was placed in the preceding section on the need for maintaining
R_h as a constant of proportionality between v_h and, respectively, i and B.
The importance of large electron mobilities for both Hall-effect based and
magnetoresistance transducers is evident from Equations (1.6) and (1.8)
because R_h is proportional to μ and $\Delta\rho/\rho_0$ is proportional to μ^2. A high
electron mobility, consistent with a low conductivity and hence a low
electron density [Equation (1.5)], is required for a maximum Hall
generator sensitivity $\partial v_h/\partial B$. Suitable materials for this purpose are the
intermetallic semiconducting compounds formed from elements in
columns III and V of the periodic table; their properties are discussed in
detail in Sections 2.1 to 2.5.

[(1)] The intermediate case, i.e. neither a complete open circuit nor a complete short
circuit of the Hall field, is treated in Section 3.2.

[(2)] Equation (1.8) may also be derived [69] by equating the work $W = i_r^2 \Delta R_r$
produced in effecting a change in the radial resistance $R_r = (\rho/2\pi d)\ln(r_2/r_1)$ with
the Joule heat $Q = v_\phi^2/R_\phi$; $v_\phi = R_h i_r B/d$ is the line integral of the circumferential
Hall field (Figure 1.2) and $R_\phi = (2\pi\rho/d)[\ln(r_2/r_1)]^{-1}$.

Metals may be ruled out of further consideration because of their high electron densities and low electron mobilities. Semiconductors have charge carriers which are activated, in part, by intrinsic processes and the rest is contributed by donor or acceptor impurities. For Hall generator applications, it is desirable to use a material with a preponderant donor impurity density N_d; these are considered to be fully ionized over the temperature range of interest. The temperature-dependent density n_i of thermally activated intrinsic electrons depends on the bandgap $\mathcal{E}_g$ at the absolute temperature T, separating the valence and conduction bands of a particular semiconductor:

$$n_i^2 = C_1 T^3 \exp\left(-\frac{\mathcal{E}_g}{kT}\right) , \qquad (1.9)$$

with the coefficient C_1 proportional to the combined density of states and k representing Boltzmann's constant. The variation in $\mathcal{E}_g$ with temperature can be represented adequately by the linear term of a series expansion. Equation (1.9) is then

$$n_i^2 = C_2 T^3 \exp\left(-\frac{\mathcal{E}_{g0}}{kT}\right) , \qquad (1.10)$$

where $\mathcal{E}_{g0}$ is the bandgap at absolute zero. Large bandgap materials appear to be more advantageous for Hall-effect and magnetoresistance-based devices because of their large values of R_h in the vicinity of 300°K, and also because of their smaller temperature dependence of R_h and σ. However, large bandgap semiconductors have low electron mobilities in comparison with the narrow gap materials, as shown in Table 2.1.

The performance of Hall generators and magnetoresistors depends not only on the ambient temperature, but also on heat evolved by current flow (Joule heat) through such devices. The linear dependence of v_h on i given in Equation (1.6) is limited by the maximum thermal dissipation which can be sustained by a Hall plate without an appreciable rise in its temperature, leading, consequently, to a dependence of R_h on i. Neglecting heat radiation and convection, let Q be the quantity of heat transferred by conduction through the two main surfaces of a Hall plate. The r.m.s. power dissipated per unit surface area is

$$Q = \frac{i_m^2 R_i}{2wl} , \qquad (1.11)$$

where R_i is the input resistance between contacts 1 and 2 of Figure 1.1 and i_m is the maximum permissible input current for $\Delta T = 0$. From Equations (1.6) and (1.11)

$$v_{hm} = wB\left(\frac{2Q}{d}\right)^{1/2}\left(\frac{\mu}{ne}\right)^{1/2} = wB(\mu R_h)^{1/2}\left(\frac{2Q}{d}\right)^{1/2} , \qquad (1.12)$$

where v_{hm} is the maximum open-circuit Hall voltage before the onset of Joule heat-induced $R_h(i)$ and consequently a nonlinear dependence of v_h on i.

Not only the density, but also the mobility of charge carriers is dependent on temperature. The thermally-induced distortion of the periodicity of crystalline lattice structure produces a temperature dependence of the mobility component μ_l due to lattice scattering of electrons, of the form $\mu_l \propto T^{-\alpha}$, with $\alpha = 1 \cdot 5$ for acoustic lattice scattering and $\alpha \approx 1 \cdot 7$ for polar optical mode scattering in materials such as InSb and InAs. The Coulomb field of ionized impurities causes electron scattering with a temperature dependence $\mu_I \propto T^{3/2}$, while impurities located in deep energy levels (un-ionized) produce a neutral scattering component of the mobility μ_N due to a localized deformation of the lattice and a temperature dependence of the type $\mu_N \propto T^{-1/2}$. Other charge carrier scattering mechanisms, such as space-charge and piezoelectric scattering, surface scattering, and electron scattering from grain boundaries, may be present to a greater or lesser extent in materials of interest for Hall generators and magnetoresistors. Assuming that the mobility components resulting from various scattering processes may be considered to be independent of each other, the effective mobility μ can be written as

$$\frac{1}{\mu} = \sum_i \frac{1}{\mu_i} . \tag{1.13}$$

The combined action of different charge carrier scattering mechanisms can produce a complex temperature dependence of μ in a semiconductor. A decrease in temperature sensitivity can be achieved by increasing N_d, the donor impurity density. This increases the relative significance of ionized impurity scattering, which, as described earlier, has a positive exponent of T, in comparison with lattice and neutral scattering processes, which have a negative exponent of T. However, an increase in impurity scattering without a compensatory decrease in the other mobility limiting factors decreases μ. Since Hall generators and magnetoresistors have a strong dependence on the effective mobility [Equations (1.6) and (1.8)], a decrease in their temperature sensitivity by impurity doping can be achieved only through some sacrifice in their performance.

The linearity between v_h and B, stated by Equation (1.6), is limited by an admixture of Hall effect and magnetoresistance phenomena. Such magnetoresistance effects may arise from the presence of two conduction bands, described in Section 3.1, or from geometrical factors, such as discussed in Section 3.2. The open-circuit Hall voltage v_h is a reciprocal function of the thickness d of a rectangular Hall plate [Equation (1.6)]. This suggests an advantage in the use of thin layers or films for Hall generators. A reduction in thickness also improves the transfer of Joule heat by conduction from both Hall generators and magnetoresistors.

However, a reduction in thickness by abrasion, lapping, or etching procedures is limited to ~10 μm owing to the brittleness of suitable semiconducting materials described in Section 2. The preparation of high-quality films with properties comparable with those of the bulk materials is feasible, but is not yet in general use. In any event, d must be kept greater than ~$5\lambda_0$, where λ_0 is the electron mean free path, so that surface scattering should not affect adversely the effective electron mobility and [in terms of Equation (1.6)] cause a reduction in v_h with d^{-1}. Thin layers and films are also desirable in order that the input and output resistances of Hall generators and the initial resistance $R(0)$ and magnetic-field-dependent resistance $R(B)$ of magnetoresistors be compatible with ancillary circuitry to which these devices are connected.

Materials and their properties

The selection of appropriate materials is one of the most important considerations in the design and construction of Hall generators and magnetoresistors. Control of their purity and homogeneity is mandatory in order to obtain required electrical and galvanomagnetic properties; however, polycrystalline materials are adequate for Hall-effect and magnetoresistance-based devices.

In large bandgap materials, grain boundaries may act as trapping centers, sources of minority carriers, and potential barriers in charge carrier transport. In bulk crystalline semiconductors, such as the intermetallic compounds InSb, InAs, and $InAs_x P_{1-x}$, grain boundaries are of negligible significance. However, grain boundaries play a major role in films; the electron mobility decreases with decreasing size of the crystallite grains. Bulk-like mobilities can be obtained only in films whose mean grain size is larger than ~ 100 μm.

Materials in which electrons are the dominant charge carriers (n-type materials) are preferable over p-type materials (conduction by holes) because of the much higher mobilities of the former, as shown in Table 2.1. InSb and InAs are the favored materials for present-day use in Hall generators and magnetoresistors. The ternary compound $InAs_{0.8}P_{0.2}$ is of interest mainly for Hall generator applications requiring a better thermal stability over a wider temperature range than that obtainable with either InSb or InAs. Silicon, used in earlier years for Hall generators, and bismuth, one of the first materials employed for magnetoresistance devices, are not in extensive use for these purposes at this time. The high electron mobility of indium antimonide makes it the most versatile material among those listed in Table 2.1. In the form of bulk crystalline

Table 2.1. Some galvanomagnetic parameters of materials for use in Hall generators and magnetoresistors.

Material	μ_n (300°K) (cm² V⁻¹ s⁻¹)	μ_p (300°K) (cm² V⁻¹ s⁻¹)	C_2	$\mathscr{E}_{g0}$ (eV)	R_h (typical) (cm³ C⁻¹)
Ge	3.9×10^3	1.9×10^3	3.1×10^{32}	0.75	-3.67×10^5
Si	1.5×10^3	5×10^2	1.5×10^{33}	1.16	-10^3
InSb	7.0×10^4	7×10^2	2.7×10^{30}	0.23	-4×10^2
InAs	2.3×10^4	2×10^2	5.6×10^{30}	0.43	-1.2×10^2
InP	4×10^3	10^2	7×10^{31}	1.41	
GaAs	5×10^3	4×10^2	5.6×10^{31}	1.52	
$InAs_{0.8}P_{0.2}$	1.2×10^4	60		0.63	-1.8×10^2
InSb (films)	6.5×10^4	7×10^2			-3×10^2
InAs (films)	$\sim 1.3 \times 10^4$				~ -100
Bi	10^7 (at 4°K)				-27 (at 4°K)

8   Chapter 2

plates, it can be used for the construction of Hall generators as well as
magnetoresistors, whose shape and electrodes are so chosen as to produce
a short circuit of the Hall field within them. The pseudobinary eutectic
alloy InSb–NiSb has needle-like NiSb inclusions within an InSb matrix.
These NiSb metallic inclusions short-circuit the Hall field in the InSb
matrix on a microscopic scale, and, in consequence, this material is
suitable for the construction of magnetoresistors. Micron-thick InSb
films can be grown from the vapor phase or by melting and solidification
of vacuum-deposited films on insulating substrates. Subminiature Hall
generators and magnetoresistors can be produced by photolithographic
procedures using such films. However, films less than ~5 μm in
thickness have electron mobilities smaller than those of bulk InSb. The
increase in the open-circuit Hall voltage due to the decrease in thickness
of a Hall plate is thus compensated by the decrease in electron mobility.
However, intrinsic or near-intrinsic InSb has a strong temperature
dependence of its electrical and galvanomagnetic properties because of the
small bandgap (Table 2.1) of InSb. In order to decrease this temperature
depedence, donor impurities (which reduce the electron mobility) must be
introduced in InSb. Indium arsenide has a larger bandgap and consequently
a reduced temperature dependence in comparison with InSb. However,
its electron mobility is much smaller than that of InSb. In consequence,
this material is not used for the construction of magnetoresistors.
Furthermore, its melting temperature and the partial vapor pressures of
its constituents are greater than those of InSb. It is a material more
difficult to grow in homogenous form than InSb and, unless grown
epitaxially, thin films have a considerably smaller electron mobility than
bulk polycrystalline InAs.

The low mobility of silicon precludes its use for magnetoresistors;
however, its bandgap, which is larger than that of InAs, leads to a smaller
temperature dependence of its electrical and galvanomagnetic parameters.
Silicon has a larger Hall coefficient than either InSb or InAs and is thus
well suited for essentially open-circuited Hall generator applications.
Standard metal-oxide-semiconductor technology and procedures can be
used for the fabrication of silicon-integrated microcircuit Hall generators,
such as described in Section 12.2. These materials, among others, suitable
for use in Hall generators and magnetoresistors, are described in further
detail in the following sections.

2.1 Indium antimonide
Indium antimonide (InSb) is a stoichiometric semiconducting compound [2]
with a zinc blende structure (lattice constant ≈6·5 Å at 300°K), a non-
parabolic conduction band centered in the Brillouin zone scheme at
$\bar{k} = 0$, and a bandgap of 0·17 eV at 300°K. The preparation of bulk
polycrystalline and single crystal InSb from the molten constituents [3] is
readily accomplished by procedures such as the Czochralski vertically-pulled

crystal technique or the horizontal Bridgeman technique. Single crystals with purities of the order of 10^{14} cm^{-3} can be grown by zone melting and refining procedures.

The low effective electron mass $m^* = 0.013m_0$ and the high electron mobility $\mu_n \approx 7 \times 10^4$ cm^2 V^{-1} s^{-1} at 300°K, the highest room temperature mobility of any known semiconductor, are of particular importance. The hole mobility at room temperature $\mu_p \approx 7 \times 10^2$ cm^2 V^{-1} s^{-1}; hence the electron-to-hole mobility ratio $b = \mu_n/\mu_p \approx 100$. For intrinsic or near-intrinsic InSb, the transport process may be described in terms of a single conduction band of electrons, as shown in Section 3.1.

The Hall coefficient of InSb is a function [4] of the relative intrinsic to impurity carrier density at any given temperature T. Figure 2.1 shows some experimentally-measured data, illustrating the dependence of R_h on T for specimens having different impurity concentrations. In the intrinsic range R_h has a logarithmic dependence on T^{-1}. An increase in the donor density N_d evidently decreases the temperature dependence of R_h in the

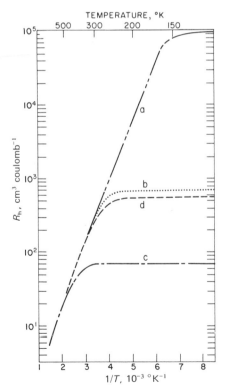

Figure 2.1. Temperature dependence of Hall coefficient of indium antimonide. Curves a, b, and c refer to bulk InSb specimens with respective impurity concentrations of ~10^{14}, 9×10^{15}, and ~10^{17} cm^{-3}; curve d is that of an InSb film (1.4×10^{16} cm^{-3}) grown by electron beam zone crystallization.

vicinity of room temperature at the expense of a lower value of R_h.
Figure 2.2 shows that the electron mobility is essentially independent of
the carrier concentration for $n < 2 \times 10^{16}$ cm^{-3}, but decreases thereafter
with n.   Figure 2.3 shows the temperature dependence of μ_n for

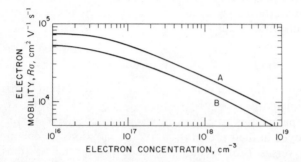

Figure 2.2. Electron mobility $\mu = R\sigma$, at 295°K, as a function of the electron
concentration.   Curve A is a composite of experimental data of Rupprecht *et al.**,
measured on bulk single crystal Te-doped InSb, and of data abstracted from Galavanov
*et al.**, measured on donor-doped bulk InSb.   Curve B shows experimental measurements
made on ~2 μm thick sulfur-doped films by Wieder and Clawson*.
* Rupprecht, H., Weber, R., Weiss, H., 1960, *Z. Naturf.*, **15a**, 783.
  Galavanov, V. V., Nasledov, D. N., Filipchenko, A. S., 1965, *Phys. Status Solidi*, 8, 671.
  Wieder, H. H., Clawson, A. R., 1968, *Solid-State Electron.*, **11**, 887.

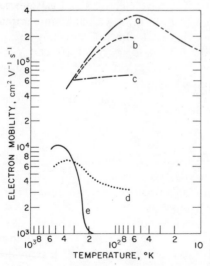

Figure 2.3. Temperature dependence of electron mobility of indium antimonide.
Curves a and b refer to bulk specimens with impurity concentrations of 8×10^{14}
and $1\cdot3 \times 10^{15}$ cm^{-3}, respectively; curve c is that of a $5\cdot2$ μm thick film
($N_d = 1\cdot2 \times 10^{16}$ cm^{-3}), grown by electron beam zone crystallization; curves d and
e are flash-evaporated films with respective impurity concentrations of 5×10^{16} and
10^{17} cm^{-3}.

specimens having different impurity concentrations [5]. The well-defined
maximum in μ_n versus T, exhibited by the relatively pure materials, is
attenuated in donor-doped InSb. The decrease in μ_n below 100°K is due
to a combination of impurity scattering and acoustic scattering, while at
higher temperatures polar optical mode lattice scattering combined with
electron–electron scattering are dominant. Above 200°K the temperature
dependence of bulk InSb with $n \approx 10^{16}$ cm^{-3} is of the form

$$\mu_n \approx 7 \cdot 7 \times 10^4 \left(\frac{T}{300}\right)^{-1 \cdot 68}. \tag{2.1}$$

Figure 2.1 shows that the temperature dependence of the Hall coefficient
of InSb films is qualitatively similar to that of bulk InSb. However, other
galvanomagnetic parameters of films are strongly dependent on the
procedures employed in their preparation. Large variations are encountered
in μ_n and in μ_n versus T of vacuum-deposited polycrystalline films
prepared under presumably identical conditions. These variations have
been correlated with the mean size of the crystallites comprising a film
by Guenther and Freller [6], by Koike and Ueda [7], and by Williamson [8].
The electron mobility increases with increasing grain size, but does not
exceed a maximum of $\sim 2 \times 10^4$ cm^2 V^{-1} s^{-1}. Furthermore, the mobility
of vacuum-deposited films has an anomalous temperature dependence, as
shown in Figure 2.3.

InSb films recrystallized by growth from the liquid phase [9] or by
electron beam crystallization [10, 11] have electrical and galvanomagnetic
properties comparable with those of bulk InSb with the same impurity
concentration. Figure 2.3 shows that such films do not have the anomaly
in μ_n versus T of vacuum-deposited films; $\mu_n \approx 6 \cdot 5 \times 10^4$ cm^2 V^{-1} s^{-1} for
$d > 5$ μm. The mean free path in InSb at 300°K is $\lambda \approx 0 \cdot 6$ μm. In
terms of Equation (1.13) it is to be expected therefore that, in addition to
the other scattering processes present in bulk InSb, surface scattering is
likely to be a mobility-limiting mechanism in films.

2.2 Indium arsenide
The structure and properties of InAs are, in many respects, similar to
those of InSb. It has a larger bandgap $\mathscr{E}_{g0} \approx 0 \cdot 44$ eV and, at 300°K,
$\mathscr{E}_g \approx 0 \cdot 35$ eV, a lattice constant of $\sim 6 \cdot 06$ Å, and a room temperature
effective mass $m^* = 0 \cdot 03 m_0$. The preparation [12] of bulk crystalline
InAs from its molten constituents is complicated by the high vapor
pressure (about 200 torr) of As at the melting point of the compound.
Small temperature variations in the vicinity of the melting point have a
large effect on the partial pressure of As over InAs.

The larger bandgap of InAs, in comparison with InSb, leads to a lower
intrinsic carrier concentration [13] at room temperature. For
$N_d \approx 5 \times 10^{16}$ cm^{-3}, the extrinsic range of InAs extends beyond +100°C,

a condition which favors its use for temperature-stabilized Hall generators. Figure 2.4 illustrates the temperature dependence of R_h of some representative specimens. At room temperature, $\mu_n \approx 2 \cdot 3 \times 10^4$ cm^2 V^{-1} s^{-1} and $\mu_p \approx 4 \cdot 5 \times 10^2$ cm^2 V^{-1} s^{-1}; the carrier concentration dependence of μ_n is essentially similar to that of InSb.

Above ~170°K, the temperature dependence of μ_n can be described [14] by a relation of the form

$$\mu_n \approx 3 \times 10^4 \left(\frac{T}{300}\right)^{-1 \cdot 2}. \tag{2.2}$$

Vacuum deposition of polycrystalline InAs films is a process made difficult by the much higher vapor pressure of As with respect to that of In, by the tendency of InAs to dissociate in vacuum, even below its melting point, and by the relatively high substrate temperatures required in order to maintain the homogeneity of the condensed layers. The temperature dependence of the Hall coefficients [6] of such films, $0 \cdot 5$ to $5 \cdot 0$ μm in thickness, is qualitatively similar to that of bulk crystalline InAs. The room temperature mobility of InAs films varies with the mean

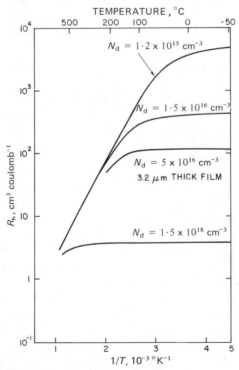

Figure 2.4. Temperature dependence of the Hall coefficient of bulk crystalline InAs and of a polycrystalline $3 \cdot 2$ μm thick film grown by a chemical vapor phase transport reaction.

size of their crystallites; nucleation and growth are essentially uncontrolled processes in nonepitaxial vacuum deposition and μ_n varies from one film to the next with the size of their crystallites. Figure 2.5 shows that the room temperature electron mobility of such films can reach values ~50% of bulk InAs with the same impurity density. The temperature dependence of μ_n, in contrast with that of vacuum-deposited InSb films, is not anomalous, as shown in Figure 2.5; the electron mobility increases as the temperature decreases.

Epitaxially-grown single-crystal InAs films [15, 16] deposited by chemical vapor-phase transport procedures onto chromium-doped insulating GaAs substrates have room temperature electron mobilities comparable with those of bulk InAs. Furthermore, their impurity concentration (10^{15} cm^{-3}) can be nearly one order of magnitude lower than those usually encountered in bulk InAs.

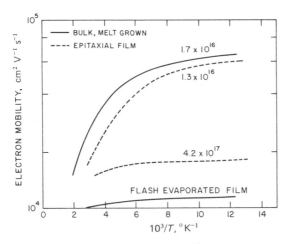

Figure 2.5. Electron mobility of bulk InAs crystals having different carrier concentrations (Harman, T. C., Goering, H. L., Beer, A. C., 1956, *Phys. Rev.,* **104**, 1562), an epitaxial film (McCarthy [16]), and a flash-evaporated film with an impurity density of 10^{17} cm^{-3}.

2.3 Indium arsenide–indium phosphide solid solutions

The solid solution of two intermetallic compounds InAs and InP has some advantages for use in Hall generators which are required to have a high degree of temperature stability at a moderate loss of magnetic field sensitivity $\partial v_h / \partial B$. A suitable composition for such applications is the solid solution InAs$_{0.8}$P$_{0.2}$, with a bandgap [17], $\mathcal{E}_{g0} = 0\cdot63$ eV, a conduction band minimum located at the center of the Brillouin zone, and a room temperature effective mass $m^* = 0\cdot02 m_0$. The Hall coefficient of InAs$_x$P$_{1-x}$ can be nearly independent of the ambient temperature in the vicinity of $300°$K, as shown in Figure 2.6.

The preparation of $InAs_x P_{1-x}$ presents a much more difficult problem than that of InAs owing to the relatively high vapor pressures of both P and As at the melting temperature of the compound [18]. Furthermore, the material grown from the liquid phase is usually inhomogenous and zone refining is needed to provide the ordered growth of the solid solution $InAs_x P_{1-x}$ on a macroscopic scale.

The temperature dependence of μ_n of $InAs_{0.8} P_{0.2}$ is also shown in Figure 2.6. At room temperature, the electron mobility is about half that of InAs. The principal mobility-limiting mechanisms are polar optical mode and ionized impurity scattering, as well as a less significant contribution from alloy scattering.

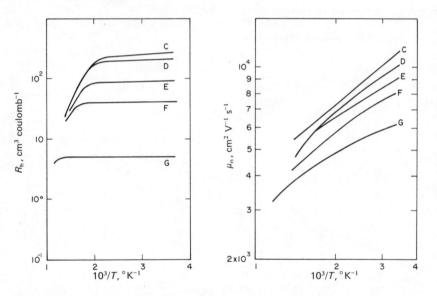

Figure 2.6. Temperature dependence of Hall coefficient and electron mobility of bulk crystalline $InAs_{0.8} P_{0.2}$ solid solutions. Curves C to G represent progressively increasing doping levels of sulfur (after Weiss [17]).

2.4 Indium antimonide–indium films

Two-phase (InSb + In) films consist of filamentary metallic In inclusions enclosed within an InSb matrix [19]. Such films can be produced by melting, by means of radiant heat, previously vacuum-codeposited layers of In and Sb containing an excess of In over the stoichiometric ratio of InSb. Rapid solidification causes InSb dendrites to grow in the form of a complex array, with In filaments trapped between them. Hall fields produced in the InSb dendrites by a transverse magnetic field are shorted by the metallic In inclusions. The resultant magnetoresistance $\Delta R/R_0$ is large and isotropic in the plane of film.

If recrystallization and synthesis of the liquid films is carried out in a unidirectional thermal gradient, then an increase in the effective values of $\Delta R/R_0$ is obtained [20] due to the preferential growth and alignment of the dendrites along this gradient; $\Delta R/R_0$ is a quadratic function of B for $B < 2$ kG, and is a linear function of B above this value. Individual dendrites have electron mobilities of $5 \cdot 7 \times 10^4$ to $5 \cdot 1 \times 10^4$ cm^2 V^{-1} s^{-1}. A further improvement and an increase in $\Delta R/R_0$ can be obtained by electron beam zone crystallization of composite (In + Sb) nonstoichiometric layers. Two-phase films 1 μm to 5 μm in thickness produced in this manner have an anisotropic magnetoresistance, as shown in Figure 2.7 [21]. Such films are suitable for the construction of thin film magnetoresistors, described in further detail in Section 5.3.

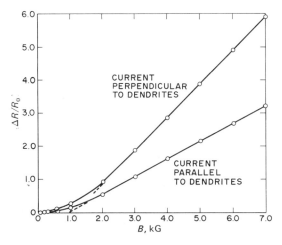

Figure 2.7. Magnetoresistance as a function of the magnetic induction of a two-phase dendritic InSb + In film grown by electron beam microzone crystallisation (after Davis and Wieder [21]).

2.5 Indium antimonide–nickel antimonide
The ternary alloy system In–Sb–Ni has a eutectic at 520°C for $1 \cdot 8$ wt.% NiSb. Directional solidification of the bulk eutectic material leads to the formation [22, 23] of metallic, NiSb needles ~50 μm long and ~1 μm diameter embedded in the semiconducting InSb matrix. The long axes of the needles are oriented along the principal thermal gradient in which this two-phase material is crystallized from its molten constituents. The conductivity of the NiSb needles is usually about two orders of magnitude greater than that of the intrinsic or lightly-doped InSb matrix, and the needles provide a short-circuit for the transverse Hall field produced in the InSb included between them. The resultant transverse magnetoresistance is anisotropic, as shown in Figure 2.8. If the current stream lines are parallel to the needle axes, then $\Delta R/R_0 \approx 0 \cdot 5$ for $B = 10$ kG, a value

commensurate with that of intrinsic homogenous InSb. If the current streamlines are perpendicular to the needle axes and the latter are oriented in parallel with B (curve b), then $\Delta R/R_0$ is slightly larger. Curve c shows that $\Delta R/R_0 \approx 18 \cdot 5$ for $B = 10$ kG, provided that the current streamlines are transverse to both the needle axes and to the magnetic induction, and curve d represents the magnetoresistance of InSb–NiSb in which the NiSb needles have a random orientation.

In order to decrease the temperature dependence of the resistivity as well as that of the magnetoresistance, the eutectic material may be doped with donor impurities. However, owing to the dependence of μ on n, this leads to a reduction in $\Delta R/R_0$. For $N_d = 1 \cdot 5 \times 10^{16}$ cm^{-3}, $\Delta R/R_0 \approx 15 \cdot 8$, and for $N_d \approx 10^{17}$ cm^{-3}, $\Delta R/R_0$ drops to a value of $\sim 3 \cdot 9$ for $B = 10$ kG.

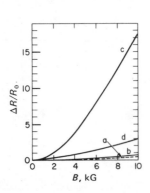
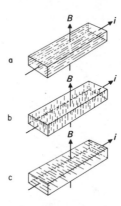

Figure 2.8. Magnetoresistance of eutectic InSb–NiSb as a function of the magnetic induction and of the orientation of the current density vector with respect to the NiSb needle axes; curves a to c correpond to the respective orientations illustrated on the right-hand side of the figure. Curve d is that of a random distribution in directional orientation of the NiSb needles (after Weiss and Wilhelm [22]).

Galvanomagnetic and thermomagnetic phenomena

Charge carriers drifting within a crystal under the action of electric and magnetic forces can be described in terms of the semiclassical equation[1]

$$m^* \frac{d\bar{v}}{dt} + m^* \bar{v} \frac{1}{\tau} = e[\bar{E} + (\bar{v} \times \bar{B})] \ , \tag{3.1}$$

where the first term represents the rate of change of momentum, the second term is a damping force proportional to the velocity of the charge carriers and the relaxation time, and τ is the mean time between collisions with the lattice or with imperfections which disturb the lattice periodicity. All the charge carriers are presumed to be in an isothermal environment and to have the same kinetic energy imparted by the electric field and by the Lorentz force. The statistical distribution in energy of the charge carriers and the energy dependence of τ are neglected.

If the magnetic induction has the single component $B = B_z$, then in terms of Figure 1.1,

$$m^* \frac{dv_x}{dt} + \frac{m^* v_x}{\tau} = e(E_x + v_y B)$$

$$m^* \frac{dv_y}{dt} + \frac{m^* v_y}{\tau} = e(E_y - v_x B)$$

$$m^* \frac{dv_z}{dt} = eE_z = 0 \ . \tag{3.2}$$

Between collisions the charge carriers traverse a fraction of a hypocycloidal path, a combination of rotational and translational motion characterized by the angular cyclotron resonance frequency, $\omega_c = eB/m^*$. Using this relation and that representing the conductivity, $\sigma = (ne^2/m^*)\tau$ in Equation (3.2),

$$\tau \frac{dJ_x}{dt} + J_x = \sigma E_x + \omega_c \tau J_y$$

$$\tau \frac{dJ_y}{dt} + J_y = \sigma E_y - \omega_c \tau J_x \ . \tag{3.3}$$

If the applied electric field and the current density are time-varying quantities with the angular frequency ω, such that $\bar{J} = \bar{J}_0 e^{i\omega t}$, then

---

[1] An account of the early theories of charge carrier transport in crystals is provided in Chapter 1 of A. H. Wilson's *The Theory of Metals*, Cambridge University Press (1958). A comprehensive account of transport phenomena in semiconductors is available in the monograph by A. C. Beer, "Galvanomagnetic effects in semiconductors", in supplement 4, *Solid State Physics (Adv. Res. Appl.)*, Eds. F. Seitz and D. Turnbull, Academic Press, New York (1963).

provided that $\overline{\nabla} \cdot E = 0$ and $\overline{\nabla} \times E = 0$, Equation (3.3) is

$$J_x(1+i\omega\tau) - \omega_c\tau J_y = \sigma E_x$$

$$J_y(1+i\omega\tau) + \omega_c\tau J_x = \sigma E_y \ . \tag{3.4}$$

Rearranging Equation (3.4) by solving explicitly for J_x and J_y leads to

$$J_x = \frac{\sigma(1+i\omega\tau)E_x}{(1+i\omega\tau)^2+(\omega_c\tau)^2} + \frac{\sigma\omega_c\tau E_y}{(1+i\omega\tau)^2+(\omega_c\tau)^2}$$

$$J_y = \frac{-\sigma\omega_c\tau E_x}{(1+i\omega\tau)^2+(\omega_c\tau)^2} + \frac{\sigma(1+i\omega\tau)E_y}{(1+i\omega\tau)^2+(\omega_c\tau)^2} \ . \tag{3.5}$$

The generalized relation between the current density and electric field vectors $\overline{J} = \hat{\sigma}\overline{E}$, may be described in terms of the conductivity tensor:

$$\hat{\sigma} = \begin{vmatrix} \sigma_{xx} & \sigma_{xy} \\ \\ -\sigma_{xy} & \sigma_{xx} \end{vmatrix} = \frac{\sigma}{(1+i\omega\tau)^2+(\omega_c\tau)^2} \begin{vmatrix} (1+i\omega\tau) & \omega_c\tau \\ \\ -\omega_c\tau & (1+i\omega\tau) \end{vmatrix} \tag{3.6}$$

At high frequencies the imaginary as well as the real components of $\hat{\sigma}$ must be taken into account. Only if $\omega\tau \ll 1$ are the tensor components

$$\sigma_{xx} = \frac{\sigma}{1+(\omega_c\tau)^2}$$

$$\sigma_{xy} = \frac{\sigma\omega_c\tau}{1+(\omega_c\tau)^2} \tag{3.7}$$

identical with those of Equation (1.3) by virtue of the fact that $\mu = (e/m^*)\tau$ and therefore $\omega_c\tau = \mu B$. For semiconducting compounds such as described in Chapter 2, τ is of the order of 10^{-12} to 10^{-13} s. Therefore σ is essentially [2] the same for d.c. and for frequencies less than ~ 10 GHz. Equations (1.5) and (3.5) were derived with the implicit assumption of prevailing isothermal conditions in the absence of thermal gradients.

Heat flow may be considered to be analogous to the flow of current in response to an electric potential gradient. The potential V is an intensive parameter whose gradients with respect to Cartesian coordinates $-\partial V/\partial x = E_x$, $-\partial V/\partial y = E_y$ produce the corresponding extensive quantities J_x and J_y. The same causal relationship connects the intensive parameter T with respect to the thermal current density ψ. The combination of galvanomagnetic and thermomagnetic phenomena [24] may

---

[2] The resistivity matrix is the reciprocal of the conductivity matrix; however, the elements of the resistivity matrix are not reciprocals of the elements of the conductivity matrix.

be represented by

$$-\frac{\partial V}{\partial x} = \rho J_x - R_h B J_y + S \psi_x - N B \psi_y$$

$$-\frac{\partial V}{\partial y} = R_h B J_x + \rho J_y + N B \psi_x + S \psi_y$$

$$-\frac{\partial T}{\partial x} = \Pi_e J_x - E_e B J_y + \rho_{th} \psi_x - L B \psi_y$$

$$-\frac{\partial T}{\partial y} = E_e B J_x + \Pi_e J_y + L B \psi_x + \rho_{th} \psi_y \ . \tag{3.8}$$

The first two equations which involve the adiabatic Hall effect include the Seebeck coefficient S and the thermomagnetic Nernst coefficient N. The last two equations include the Peltier coefficient Π_e and the thermal resistivity ρ_{th} (the reciprocal of the thermal conductivity), as well as the Ettingshausen coefficient E_e and the Righi–Leduc coefficient L.

It is apparent from Equations (3.8) that all transverse 'resistivities' are proportional to B and exhibit oblique symmetry $\rho_{ij} = -\rho_{ji}$ in accordance with Onsager's relations [25, 26], $\rho_{ij}(\bar{B}) = \rho_{ji}(-\bar{B})$, which in irreversible thermodynamics are the counterpart of the second law of thermodynamics.

Potentials generated by thermoelectric and thermomagnetic phenomena are usually negligible or of second order in comparison with transverse Hall voltages or magnetoresistance effects, unless large thermal gradients are unavoidably present. It is important, therefore, to reduce such gradients to a minimum in Hall effect and magnetoresistance transducers. Design techniques suggested for this purpose are described in Chapter 4.

3.1 Isothermal Ohm–Hall equations

A homogenous isotropic semiconductor in zero magnetic field and in an isothermal environment can be described in terms of the scalar conductivity σ or the scalar resistivity ρ. In the presence of a magnetic field, the conductivity and resistivity become tensor quantities characterized by the Ohm–Hall equations

$$\bar{E} = \rho \bar{J} - R_h (\bar{J} \times \bar{B})$$

$$\bar{J} = \sigma \bar{E} - \sigma R_h (\bar{J} \times \bar{B}) \ . \tag{3.9}$$

In zero magnetic field, the current streamlines are normal to the equipotential planes in a Hall plate such as shown in Figure 1.1. In a magnetic field the equipotential planes are rotated with respect to the current streamlines by an angle ϕ, defined as the Hall angle. It is the angle between the effective electric field $\bar{E}$ and the current density $\bar{J}$, and can be derived analytically from the second of the two equations in Equations (3.9) by multiplying it by $\bar{E}$:

$$\bar{J} \times \bar{E} = \sigma (\bar{E} \times \bar{E}) - \sigma R_h [(\bar{J} \times \bar{B}) \times \bar{E}] \ . \tag{3.10}$$

From Equation (3.10), with the magnetic induction transverse to the applied electric field, the tangent of the Hall angle (negative for electrons and positive for holes) is

$$\tan\phi = -\sigma R_h B .\qquad (3.11)$$

For a single conduction band, $R_h = \pm\mu/\sigma$; therefore $\tan\phi = \pm\mu B$. If electrons and holes contribute to the effective conductivity, then due account must be taken of the different Hall fields and Hall angles, as shown in Figure 3.1; terms denoted by the subscript n are due to electrons and those described by the subscript p are due to holes. For small Hall angles ($B \to 0$)

$$\phi_n \approx -\mu_n B \qquad \phi_p \approx \mu_p B .\qquad (3.12)$$

The Hall current J_y is the vector sum of the electron current density $-J_n \sin\phi_n$ and of the hole current density $-J_p \sin\phi_p$; for small Hall angles

$$J_y \approx -(J_n \phi_n + J_p \phi_n) .\qquad (3.13)$$

The effective Hall angle $\phi \approx J_y/J_x$; therefore, by means of Equations (3.12) and (3.13),

$$\phi \approx \left(\frac{n\mu_n^2 - p\mu_p^2}{n\mu_n + p\mu_p} \right) B .\qquad (3.14)$$

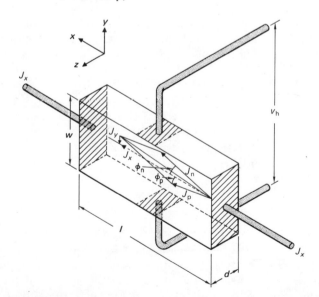

Figure 3.1. Vector diagram of electron current density J_n, hole current density J_p, and Hall current density J_y in a Hall plate. The magnetic induction is along the z axis; ϕ_n and ϕ_p are the Hall angles pertaining, respectively, to electrons and holes; J_x is the resultant current density along the x axis; and v_h is the Hall voltage output.

For negligibly small magnetic fields, the two-band Hall coefficient R_{h0}, in terms of the electron-to-hole mobility ratio $b = \mu_n/\mu_p$ and Equation (3.11), is

$$R_{h0} = -\frac{1}{e}\left(\frac{nb^2 - p}{(nb+p)^2}\right).\tag{3.15}$$

For InSb and InAs in the intrinsic and near intrinsic range, where $n \approx p$ and $b \gg 1$, Equation (3.15) leads to the Hall coefficient of the single band of electrons, $R_h \approx -1/ne$, of Equation (1.5).

In appreciable magnetic fields, materials, in which two different electron bands or electron and hole bands participate in the conduction process, have Hall coefficients which depend on the magnetic induction [27, 28] and have magnetoresistance components $(\Delta R/R_0)_P$ of 'physical' origin, i.e. not connected with the 'geometrical' short circuit of the Hall field. These results can be derived analytically from the Ohm–Hall equations of each distinct band, neglecting cross interactions between them and summing the current density components of the corresponding terms of the conductivity matrices [Equation (3.6)]:

$$R_h(B) = R_{h0}\left(\frac{1 - Z\mu_n^2 B^2}{1 + Y\mu_n^2 B^2}\right)$$

$$\left(\frac{\Delta R}{R_0}\right)_P = \frac{X\mu_n^2 B^2}{1 + Y\mu_n^2 B^2},\tag{3.16}$$

where the parameters X, Y, and Z are, respectively,

$$X = \frac{c(b+1)^2}{b(1+bc)^2},\qquad Y = \left(\frac{1-c}{1+bc}\right)^2,\qquad Z = \frac{1-c}{b^2c-1},\tag{3.17}$$

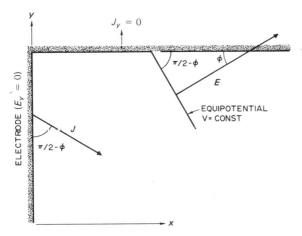

Figure 3.2. Boundary conditions for a rectangular Hall plate in a homogeneous magnetic field.

and c is the ratio of electron-to-hole concentration, $c = n/p$.

The presence of acceptor impurity centers is not desirable in materials used for Hall generator applications; Equations (3.16) and (3.17) show that they can cause a magnetic field dependence of R_h. They can also cause a reduction in μ_n due to scattering of electrons from the ionized impurity centers. The magnetoresistance of two-band materials $(\Delta R/R_0)_P$ is dependent on the acceptor density [29, 30]. However, its magnitude in InSb and InAs is slight in comparison with the geometrical magnetoresistance $(\Delta R/R_0)_G$ described in the next section. The latter is of primary importance for the construction of magnetoresistors and magnetoresistance transducers.

3.2 Geometrical factors

The significance of the geometrical configuration of a rectangular Hall plate or magnetoresistor, in particular its length-to-width ratio and the shape, size, and position of its electrodes has been tacitly ignored in previous sections. Intuitively, it might be expected that the input current electrodes, which cover the cross-sectional surface areas of a Hall plate such as shown in Figure 1.1, might short-circuit the Hall field in their immediate vicinity; this ought to produce a complementary magnetoresistance and, while the effect is likely to be strong near the electrodes, it should be negligible in the center of the Hall plate.

The relative contribution of Hall field and magnetoresistance can be assessed from the electric field and current flux line distributions. In the steady state, $\partial \bar{B}/\partial t = 0$, $B = B_z$, and $\nabla \times \bar{E} = 0$. If no charge sources or sinks are present within the plate, then $\nabla \cdot \bar{J} = 0$ and, with $\bar{J} = \hat{\sigma}\bar{E}$, $\hat{\sigma}(\nabla \cdot \bar{E}) = 0$. The electric field $\bar{E}$ is the negative gradient of the potential function $V(x, y, z)$, and with $\partial V/\partial z = 0$ the above leads to Laplace's equation,

$$\frac{\partial^2 V}{\partial x^2} + \frac{\partial^2 V}{\partial y^2} = 0 \; , \tag{3.18}$$

which is to be solved subject to specified boundary conditions. These are illustrated in Figure 3.2 for a rectangular plate: $J_y = 0$ for $y = w$ or 0 and for $0 < x < l$; the input current electrodes are considered to be equipotential planes, $V = $ const. From the Ohm–Hall Equations (3.9), it is evident that for $J_y = 0$ the angle between the x axis and $\bar{E}$ is the Hall angle ϕ. The current density vector $\bar{J}$ enters the Hall plate from the current electrodes at an angle $\frac{1}{2}\pi - \phi$, and within the plate the equipotential planes are rotated with respect to the current streamlines.

A number of different techniques may be used for solving the boundary value problem of Equation (3.18). One of these, conformal mapping [31–34], employs the Schwarz–Christoffel transformation [43]. Another, a relaxation method [35–37], consists in covering the region of the Hall plate with a square grid mesh so chosen that the boundaries coincide with nodes of the grid. Laplace's equation is then replaced by a set of finite difference equations, and matrix inversion methods [38] may be used to solve these on a digital computer. The results of such calculations indicate that the Hall voltage v_h, defined by Equation (1.6), is valid only if the length-to-width ratio of the rectangular plate $l/w \to \infty$. The geometrical correction factor F for v_h is a function of the Hall angle ϕ and of l/w:

$$v_h = R_h \frac{Bi}{d} F(l/w, \phi) . \tag{3.19}$$

This function is represented graphically [34] in Figure 3.3; v_h is normalized in terms of $v_{h\infty}$, the Hall voltage of an infinitely long specimen [Equation (1.6)], and the Hall electrodes are presumed to be point contacts. The relative position x/l of the Hall electrodes along the boundaries between the input electrodes also determine [39–41] the effective magnitude of $v_h/v_{h\infty}$, as shown in Figure 3.4. Near the current electrodes, the Hall field is electrostatically short-circuited; the gradient $\partial(v_h/v_{h\infty})/\partial(x/l)$ is large but decreases towards the center of the Hall plate, and it is essentially independent of μB for $l/w \gtrsim 3$.

It is reasonable to expect from the complementarity of the Hall effect and magnetoresistance that, for $l/w \to 0$, the electrostatically short-circuited Hall field should approach, in the limit, a 'geometrical' magnetoresistance component $(\Delta R/R_0)_G$, such as that of a Corbino disc [Figure 1.2 and Equation (1.8)]. The magnetic field-dependent resistance $R(B)$ between the fully electroded faces of a rectangular plate is

$$R(B) = \rho(B)\frac{l}{wd} G(l/w, \phi) \tag{3.20}$$

where $G(l/w, \phi)$ is the geometry-dependent correction factor to be

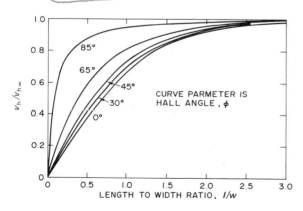

Figure 3.3. Normalized Hall output voltage of a rectangular plate as a function of length-to-width ratio l/w and Hall angle ϕ.

determined from a solution of Laplace's equation and $\rho(B)$ is the magnetic field-dependent resistivity. Equation (3.20) may be written in the form

$$R(B) = \frac{R(0)\rho(B)}{\rho(0)} G(l/w, \phi) \ . \tag{3.21}$$

For a single conduction band, $\rho(B) = \rho(0)$, and Equation (3.21) is then

$$\left(\frac{\Delta R}{R_0}\right)_G = G(l/w, \phi) - 1 \ . \tag{3.22}$$

The function $G(l/w, \phi)$ has been evaluated by means of conformal mapping [32–34] as well as by the method of finite differences [35–38]. Although conformal mapping does not provide, in closed form, analytical solutions over the entire range of $\tan\phi$, it appears to be more accurate than the latter method. For small Hall angles, $\mu_n B \leqslant 0\cdot45$, the magnetoresistance calculated using either method is quadratic in B and it is linear in B for $\phi \to \frac{1}{2}\pi$. Figure 3.5 illustrates the dependence of $(\Delta R/R_0)_G$ on $\mu_n B$, with l/w as a parameter, calculated by Lippmann and Kuhrt [32]. Clearly, as $l/w \to 0$, the value $(\Delta R/R_0)_G$ approaches that of a Corbino disc. The curve is in good agreement with experiment [42], and electrostatic shorting of the Hall field by an appropriate choice of geometrical parameters is the basis for the raster pattern magnetoresistor configuration described in Chapter 5.

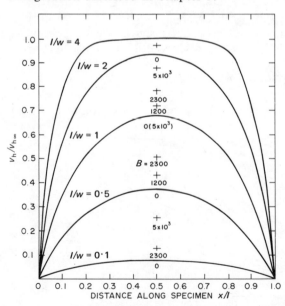

Figure 3.4. Normalized Hall output voltage as a function of position of Hall electrodes along the length of a rectangular Hall plate ($\mu_n = 6 \times 10^4$ cm^2 V^{-1} s^{-1}); the length-to-width ratio and applied magnetic fields (in gauss) are also indicated (after Beer, A. C., 1963, *Galvanomagnetic Effects in Semiconductors* (Academic Press, New York).

The geometrical correction factor $F(l/w, \phi) = v_h/v_{h\infty}$ was derived with the initial assumption that Hall electrodes of a rectangular Hall plate may be represented adequately by equispaced point contacts which do not perturb the distribution of equipotentials and current streamlines. In practice, Hall electrodes with finite dimensions of the order s (with $s/l \approx 0\cdot1$) have an appreciable effect [31, 40, 44] on the Hall field and consequently on the actual linearity between v_h and B.

The impedance between the Hall electrodes was calculated by Endsley et al. [45] with the initial assumptions: (1) the Hall angle is zero; (2) the dimension s (along l) of a Hall electrode is much smaller than l; (3) the electrodes cover the entire thickness dimension d of the rectangular plate. These calculations were extended by Datta and Daw [46] to Hall contacts of arbitrary size and subsequently [47] to electrodes offset with respect to each other. Haeusler and Lippmann [48] give an approximate analytical function which takes into account the combined geometrical dependence of the Hall electrodes and that of the input current electrodes of the form:

$$F(l/w, s/w, \phi) = \left[1 - \exp\left(-\frac{\pi l}{2w}\frac{\phi}{\tan\phi}\right)\right]\left(1 - \frac{2s}{\pi w}\frac{\phi}{\tan\phi}\right), \qquad (3.23)$$

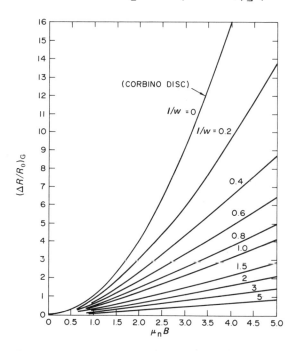

Figure 3.5. Geometrical magnetoresistance $(\Delta R/R_0)_G$ of a rectangular n-type plate [Equation (3.22)] measured between its current electrodes, as a function of Hall tangent and length-to-width ratio (after Lippmann, H. J., Kuhrt, F., 1958, Z. Naturf., 13a, 474).

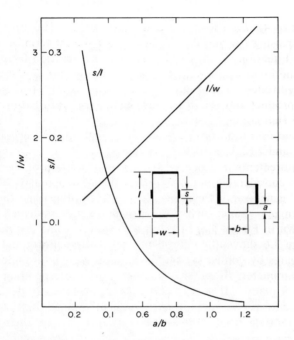

Figure 3.6. A comparison between equivalent geometrical correction factors for rectangular and cruciform Hall plates (after Haeusler, J., Lippmann, H. J., 1968, *Solid-State Electron.*, **11**, 173).

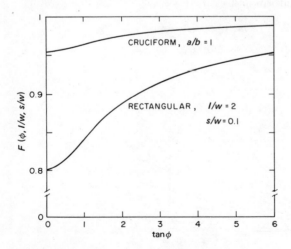

Figure 3.7. Geometrical correction factor for a specific rectangular Hall plate in comparison with that of a cruciform plate as a function of Hall tangents (after Haeusler, J., Lippmann, H. J., 1968, *Solid-State Electron.*, **11**, 173).

to within an error of 4% for $l/w \geqslant 1 \cdot 5$ and $s/w = 0 \cdot 18$. The error decreases with increasing l/w and decreasing s/w. The first term on the right-hand side of Equation (3.23) is the geometrical correction factor $F(l/w, \phi)$ due to the input current electrodes, and the second $F(s/w, \phi)$ is due to the Hall electrodes. The resultant geometrical factor $F(l/w, s/w, \phi)$ is evidently their product and the dominant term is the perturbation introduced by the Hall contacts. For example, if $\phi = 0$, $l/w = 2$, and $s/w = 0 \cdot 1$, then the first term in Equation (3.23) is $0 \cdot 93$, the second has the value $0 \cdot 8725$, and $F(2, 0 \cdot 1, 0) = 0 \cdot 81$.

Meeting the requirements imposed by the size and position of the Hall electrodes leads to considerable practical difficulties in design and fabrication of Hall generators. Devices with a contour other than the conventional rectangular shape, such as the symmetrical cross-shaped configuration shown in Figure 3.6, offer, in this respect, some distinct advantages. Figure 3.6 shows the equivalence [48] of cruciform and rectangular Hall plates by comparing the geometrical correction factors and l/w and s/w parameters of rectangular plates with corresponding a/b factors of cruciform plates. It is not only easier to make electrodes and attach leads to cruciform plates, it is also convenient to have the Hall electrodes and current electrodes interchangeable; furthermore, their correction factors have a much smaller dependence upon the magnetic induction, as shown in Figure 3.7, and therefore a smaller linearity error than rectangular plates. Haeusler and Lippmann [48] have shown this to be the case experimentally, and similar results were obtained by Halla [49] on cruciform and maltese cross-shaped Hall generators.

Hall generator circuit parameters

Hall plates, usually less than 100 μm in thickness, are prepared from bulk crystalline materials by abrasion, lapping, and etching techniques. They are attached, thereafter, to an insulating ceramic wafer, having a matching thermal expansion coefficient, which provides the requisite mechanical support and protection for the fragile Hall plate. Figure 4.1 (facing p.54) shows a partially assembled Hall generator, with leads attached, before the protective cover plate, of the same ceramic material as the substrate, is placed over it. Thin films of the intermetallic III–V compounds on insulating substrates, used for the construction of miniature and subminiature Hall generators, provide a considerable advantage over the corresponding bulk materials because photolithographic techniques can be used for the production of complex shapes, such as the high-resolution Hall probe shown in Figure 4.2. The input and output impedances of thin film Hall generators may be tailored for a specific requirement by an appropriate choice of film thickness. Furthermore, the dissipation of Joule heat by radiation and conduction is more effective in thin films than bulk crystalline materials.

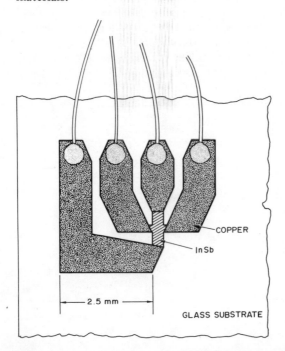

Figure 4.2. Miniature Hall generator produced by photolithographic process, starting with an electron beam zone-crystallized InSb film on its glass substrate, etching a specific contour, and plating copper electrodes on its sidearms.

A Hall generator is a four-pole circuit element and can be described in terms of its input and output parameters as

$$v_1 = R_{11}i_1 + R_{12}i_2$$
$$v_2 = R_{21}i_1 + R_{22}i_2 , \tag{4.1}$$

where the first of the above equations refers to the input circuit, with i_1 the input current produced by the applied voltage v_1, and R_{11} is the driving-point (input) resistance defined in terms of $R_{11} = (v_1/i)_{i_2 = 0}$ The transfer resistance $R_{12} = (v_1/i_2)_{i_1 = 0}$, i.e. it is the result of a Hall voltage generated across the open-circuited input terminals for a current i_2 applied across the output terminals. If electrons are the dominant charge carriers, then $R_{12} = -(R_h B/d) \times 10^{-8}$ ohms, where R_h is given in cm³ C⁻¹, B is in gauss, and d in cm. The second equation of Equations (4.1) is that of the output circuit. Owing to the nonreciprocity of the Hall effect [31, 50], the transfer resistance $R_{21} = -R_{12}$ and the parameter $R_{22} = (v_2/i_2)_{i_1 = 0}$ is the unloaded output resistance of the Hall generator. A Hall generator loaded by a resistance R_L across the Hall terminals has an input resistance R_{in}, an output resistance R_{out} and respective voltage and current gains A_v and A_i [1]:

$$R_{in} = \frac{\delta R + R_{11}R_L}{R_{22} + R_L} , \qquad A_v = \frac{R_{21}R_L}{\delta R + R_{11}R_L}$$

$$R_{out} = \frac{\delta R + R_{22}R_g}{R_{11} + R_g} , \qquad A_i = \frac{-R_{21}}{R_{22} + R_L} , \tag{4.2}$$

where R_g is the internal resistance of the generator (source) providing the input voltage v_1 and $\delta R = R_{11}R_{22} - R_{12}R_{21}$.

The four-pole parameters of Equation (4.2), together with the nominal input current, the misalignment potential between Hall electrodes, the magnetic field and input current linearity, and their temperature dependence, discussed in detail in the following sections, constitute the significant criteria which determine the operational performance of Hall generators.

4.1 Residual misalignment voltage

An arbitrarily-shaped Hall plate, such as shown in Figure 4.3, with input current electrodes 1 and 2 and point-contact Hall electrodes 3 and 4, has a residual output voltage v_o if the latter contacts are not aligned on the same equipotential plane in zero magnetic field. Let the two equipotential planes in Figure 4.3 extend across 3 and 3′, 4 and 4′

---

[1] A detailed calculation of the four-pole parameters of InSb Hall generators is provided in [45].

$(B \neq 0)$; then the output voltage, v_o between Hall electrodes 3 and 4 is

$$v_2 = (v_3 - v_4) = (v_3 - v_3') + (v_3' - v_4)$$

$$v_h = v_3 - v_3'$$

$$v_o = v_3' - v_4 . \tag{4.3}$$

If a resistance r_o is defined in terms of the current and potential drop between the equipotential planes 3 and 4, then $v_o = i_1 r_o$. For i_1 derived from a current source, r_o, and consequently v_o, changes with temperature owing to the dependence of σ on T. A physical or geometrical magneto-resistance also affects [60] r_o, and consequently v_o is also dependent on the magnetic induction B. For a Hall generator driven from a voltage source, v_1 is constant; consequently $v_o = v_1 (r_o / r_{11})$ and the temperature dependence of r_o and of r_{11} are the same. Therefore v_o is independent of temperature. However, r_o and r_{11} do not have the same dependence on B owing to their different geometrical configurations. Therefore v_o is also a function of their relative geometrical factors as well as of B.

Compensation of the residual misalignment potential can be achieved by means of two different procedures: (1) circuits external to the Hall generator providing a voltage equal and opposite to v_o; (2) multiple input current electrodes so driven that points 3 and 4 can be brought to be on the same equipotential plane in zero magnetic field.

Figure 4.4 is a schematic representation of circuits suitable for compensating the misalignment potential provided that the input current i_1 remains essentially unaffected by the shunt circuit. The condition $i_c \ll i_1$ requires that $r \gg r_{33}'$ or that $r \gg r_{13}$. Once adjusted for a null, the compensation is stable with temperature for all three circuit configurations; however, only that shown in Figure 4.4b can be made to be independent of B, because for this circuit $r_{33}'(B)$ is analogous to $r_o(B)$,

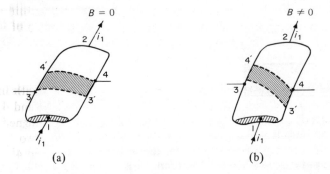

$B = 0$ $B \neq 0$

(a)   (b)

Figure 4.3. Arbitrarily-shaped Hall generator with residual misalignment potential v_o between Hall electrodes 3 and 4: (a) in zero magnetic field; dashed lines are equipotentials; (b) misalignment voltage and rotation of equipotential planes in finite magnetic field.

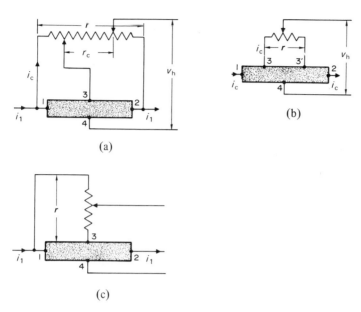

Figure 4.4. Three different methods for compensating the residual misalignment voltage in Hall generators driven by a constant current source (after Fraenkel and Gruen [54]).

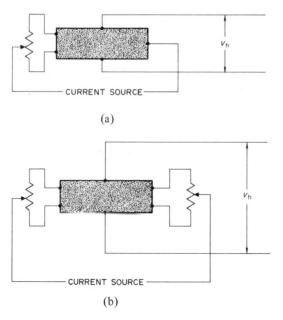

Figure 4.5. Compensation of residual misalignment voltage by means of multiple input current electrodes (after Roth and Straub [52]); impedance of external current-divider network must be large compared with Hall generator impedance.

and the position of electrodes 3 and 3' can be adjusted so as to reduce the magnetic field dependence of v_o to a negligible value.

Compensation of the misalignment voltage by multiple current electrodes is illustrated in Figure 4.5. The circuit shown in Figure 4.5a is advantageous, in comparison with those shown in Figure 4.4, in that arbitrary impedances are excluded from the output circuit. The misalignment voltage is essentially independent of T; however, it is dependent on B and it is a quadratic function of the input current. The misalignment voltage can be reduced to a negligible value in the circuit shown in Figure 4.5b; furthermore, it is independent of the amplitude of the input current. Both circuits do not yield an output voltage v_2 strictly proportional to the product $i_1 B$. The deviation from linearity increases with B and reaches a value of ~10% at 10^4 gauss. Experimental measurements [51–54] made on a variety of circuit configurations, including those shown in Figures 4.4 and 4.5, suggest that in terms of the thermal variation and magnetic field dependence of the misalignment voltage, the circuit shown in Figure 4.4b is the most advantageous.

4.2 The input current

The nominal input current of Hall generators is usually specified in terms of an allowable rise in temperature, produced by Joule heating, referenced with respect to an ambient temperature of $+25°C$ in still air[2] with $B \rightarrow 0$.

Bulk crystalline Hall generators available commercially have nominal input currents of the order of $0 \cdot 1$ A, while thin film Hall generators have input currents of the order of 10 to 50 mA, depending on material and film thickness. The maximum allowable d.c. input current i_{max} is determined by the onset of a deviation from linearity $v_h(i)$, described in Section 1.1. An increase of one to two orders in magnitude in i_{max} can be obtained by driving Hall generators with low-duty cycle pulsed [55, 56] input currents i_p. If i_{dc} is the peak d.c. current defined in terms of the average Joule heat dissipated by a Hall generator, then for rectangular current pulses of duration τ_1 and interval between pulses of τ_2

$$i_p = i_{dc} \left(1 + \frac{\tau_2}{\tau_1}\right)^{\frac{1}{2}} . \tag{4.4}$$

A critical factor which determines the maximum pulse repetition rate $\nu = (\tau_1 + \tau_2)^{-1}$ is the thermal time constant [57] $\tau_{th} = C_{th} R_{th}$, where C_{th} is the thermal capacity and R_{th} the thermal resistance of a Hall generator. C_{th} is a function of the specific gravity (~5·5 g cm^{-3} for InAs), specific heat (~$6 \cdot 4 \times 10^{-2}$ cal g^{-1} deg^{-1} for InAs), and of the volume occupied

---

[2] In high magnetic fields the magnetoresistance effect produces a further rise in nondissipated Joule heat. The nominal input current must be derated to take this effect into account.

by a Hall generator. The latter factor is considerably reduced in the case of thin films. Furthermore, the large surface-to-volume ratio facilitates the transfer of Joule heat. An order-of-magnitude decrease in thermal time constant can be obtained in InSb Hall generators in comparison with bulk InSb having the same surface area, and a further decrease up to an order of magnitude can be obtained by bonding a thin film Hall generator (active area 100 μm × 40 μm) to copper plates 1 cm × 1 cm in area and 100 μm in thickness.

4.3 Temperature dependence

The electrical and galvanomagnetic coefficients of semiconducting materials employed for the construction of Hall generators and magnetoresistors are temperature-dependent. Consequently, the resistances of magnetoresistors, the Hall coefficients, input and output resistances, and the misalignment voltages of Hall generators are dependent on the Joule heat evolved by the currents flowing through them as well as on the ambient temperature T. If such devices are to have a temperature-independent response over a range such as $-20°C$ to $+50°C$, then they must be made of materials with sufficiently large energy bandgaps so that intrinsically generated carriers represent a negligible fraction of the total carrier density in this temperature region. In III–V compound n-type semiconductors, the donor impurity density must be high enough to extend the extrinsic range to $\sim+50°C$. However, such a procedure leads to a decrease in sensitivity and efficiency owing to the lower electron mobility produced by ionized impurity scattering. An alternative procedure is to use other circuit elements in conjunction with Hall generators and magnetoresistors in order to compensate for their temperature dependence. Loading the output terminals of a Hall generator with a linear resistance R_L in series with a thermistor R_τ can produce such a compensation. The temperature-dependent output voltage $v_{hL}(T)$ measured across R_L is then

$$v_{hL}(T) = \frac{v_{ho}(T)}{1 + [R_{22}(T) + R_\tau(T)]/R_L} \ . \tag{4.5}$$

If a Hall generator is to be independent of temperature variations between the limits T_1 and T_2, then $v_{hL}(T_1) = v_{hL}(T_2)$, and this condition must be maintained over a defined extent of B and i_1. The temperature coefficient of resistance of R_τ and the value of R_L must be chosen, in terms of Equation (4.5), so that $(dv_{hL}/dT) = 0$.

The Hall coefficients of InAs and $InAs_x P_{1-x}$ have a negative temperature coefficient $-(1/R_h)dR_h/dT$, while the temperature coefficients of their internal impedances, for example $(1/R_{11})dR_{11}/dT$, are positive. Circuital compensation of thermal variations in v_{hL} can be effected by means of a thermistor with an appropriate negative temperature coefficient of resistance.

In contrast with InAs and $InAs_x P_{1-x}$, Hall generators made of intrinsic InSb have negative temperature coefficients of their internal resistances as well as their Hall coefficients. A limited circuital temperature compensation, in terms of Equation (4.5), can be achieved by an appropriate choice of R_L and by dispensing with R_r. A different temperature compensation method for intrinsic InSb is the substitution of a voltage source v_i for the current source, which provides the Hall generator input current i_1. Silverman [257] has applied such a procedure for the thermal compensation of InSb film Hall generators. Defining the temperature dependences of R_h and R_{11} between $+25°C$ and $+100°C$ by a relation of the form

$$R_h = k_1 \exp(-\beta_1 T)$$

$$R_{11} = k_2 \exp(-\beta_2 T) ,   \qquad (4.6)$$

then the open-circuit Hall voltage v_{ho} is, in consequence,

$$v_{ho} = \frac{k_1}{k_2} \frac{v_i B}{d} \exp[(\beta_2 - \beta_1)T] .   \qquad (4.7)$$

The exponential term in Equation (4.7) is considerably smaller than that of a Hall generator driven by a current source whose open-circuit Hall voltage is proportional to $\exp(-\beta_1 T)$. For the vacuum deposited InSb films used by Silverman, $\beta_1 = 0·014$ deg^{-1} and $\beta_2 = 0·017$ deg^{-1}. A further improvement in temperature compensation is to be expected from a resistively loaded Hall generator. Using a matched load resistance [257] and a voltage source for a film Hall generator, the variation in v_{hL} is, at most, $4·8\%$ between $0°C$ and $100°C$; it is $+35\%$ for the open-circuited Hall generator and $-75·3\%$ with the same device driven by a current source, over the same temperature range. A different method of compensation, suitable for use with InSb Hall generators with high internal resistances ($\sim 10^3$ Ω) driven from voltage sources, was described by Balanov et al. [258]. A resistor with a positive temperature coefficient of resistance, such as copper, is connected in series with the Hall generator whose temperature dependence is to be compensated over a restricted range, $+10°C$ to $+45°C$. Experimental data and calculated values derived in terms of Equation (4.6) and the condition $i_1 R_h(T) = $ const. are in good agreement; the open-circuit Hall voltage was found to be independent of temperature (within $1·1\%$) over the above-cited temperature range.

A simple compensation of the temperature-dependent open-circuit Hall voltage of n-type InAs and $InAs_x P_{1-x}$ Hall generators can be made by shunting their input terminals with linear resistances having positive temperature coefficients of resistance. Nickel wire resistors with an essentially constant coefficient of $\sim 0·5\%$ deg^{-1} (between $0°$ and $+100°C$) are well suited for this purpose. The open-circuit output voltage of a Hall generator, whose input terminals are shunted by such a nickel resistor

$R_N(T)$, can be expressed as

$$v_h = \frac{v_{ho}(T)}{1 + R_{11}(T)/R_N(T)} \tag{4.8}$$

where $v_{ho}(T)$ is the Hall output voltage without the shunt resistor in the circuit.

In a magnetic field, the current density in Hall generators and magnetoresistors is distributed inhomogenously. Localized Joule heating produces large thermal gradients, and these, in turn, can affect the electrical and galvanomagnetic properties of the devices. The thermocouple junctions between the semiconductor plates and their metallic electrodes also produce a significant Peltier effect. Gruetzmann [259] calculated the temperature distribution in rectangular Hall plates and magnetoresistors as a function of their geometrical configuration, thermal and electrical parameters, and the magnetic induction. The analysis, supported by experimental investigations [260], indicates that the principal error in d.c. or a.c. Hall measurements is that due to the inhomogenous temperature distribution. Error voltage components of the order of 2% appear across the output terminals of InSb Hall plates ($l/w = 2$ and $\phi = 45$). The contribution of the Peltier effect at d.c. or low frequency a.c. (<10 Hz) causes an increase in this error to ~3% and the temperature difference near a current electrode was found to increase by a factor of 19 in large Hall angles ($\phi = 80°$) over that measured on the same Hall plate in zero magnetic field.

In magnetoresistors, the spacing between current electrodes ($l/w \ll 1$) is much smaller than in Hall generators. This leads to an essentially homogenous temperature distribution between them, irrespective of Joule heating. However, the dependence of the resistance on the magnetic induction does produce an increase in heat that must be dissipated by a magnetoresistor driven from a constant current source if its temperature is not to rise with B.

The inhomogenous temperature distribution in Hall generators and other thermoelectric or thermomagnetic perturbations present in magnetoresistors can be reduced to a negligible value [58] by appropriate geometrical configurations, such as shown in Figure 4.6.

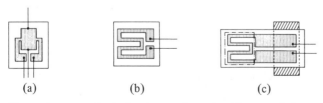

(a)   (b)   (c)

Figure 4.6. A method of reducing thermal gradients and thermoelectric error voltages in Hall generators (a), and magnetoresistors (b) and (c), by an appropriate geometrical configuration (after Weiss, H., US Patent 3 264 861, issued 12 July 1966).

4.4 Sensitivity and linearity

The open-circuit magnetic field sensitivity γ_{OB} of a Hall generator can be defined as $\gamma_{OB} = v_h/B$. It is not linear in B owing to the geometrical magnetoresistance of the input current and Hall electrodes discussed in Section 3.2. For a rectangular Hall generator with finite l/w and s/w ratios, the open-circuit sensitivity is smaller than the idealized value [Equation (1.6) derived under the assumption of point-contact Hall electrodes]. In low and moderate magnetic fields γ_{OB} rises nonlinearly with B, the curve having a concave characteristic. Cruciform Hall generators have a much smaller inherent nonlinearity of γ_{OB} versus B than rectangular devices, as shown experimentally by Halla [49] and by Haeusler and Lippmann [48].

Loading Hall generator output terminals with a resistance R_L has an effect upon its input resistance as well as upon its sensitivity γ_{LB} The output voltage developed across R_L is $v_{hL} = i_2 R_L$, and

$$\gamma_{LB} = \frac{(-R_h/d)i_1 F(l/w, s/w, \phi)}{1 + R_{22}/R_L} . \tag{4.9}$$

While γ_{LB} approaches γ_{OB} for $R_L \gg R_{22}$, it decreases with R_L and depends on B, not only because of its dependence on the Hall angle, but also because R_{22} is itself a function of the magnetic induction. Furthermore, an appreciable Hall current i_2 brings about a transverse magnetoresistance with a consequent reduction in the Hall field. This causes a convex nonlinear dependence of γ_{LB} on B in high magnetic inductions. The combination of the geometrical factor-dependent nonlinearity (concave) and Hall current nonlinearity (convex) gives rise to an S-shaped γ_{LB} versus B curve. The optimum value of the load resistance R_{LO} is that which minimizes the excursions of the γ_{LB} versus B curve about a 'best fit' straight line [50]. The linearity error may be expressed in percent of full scale of the range of linear compensation or in terms of curves, such as shown in Figure 4.7, which represents the percent nonlinearity of reading [59] calibrated by comparison with an inherently linear instrument, such as a rotating-coil gaussmeter.

The static current sensitivity γ_i is the ratio of the Hall output voltage to the input current which produced it for a given magnitude of the magnetic induction:

$$\gamma_i = \frac{v_h}{i_1} , \qquad B = \text{const.} \tag{4.10}$$

Definitions [59, 261, 262] applicable to γ_{Oi} and γ_{Li} are analogous to those given earlier for the open-circuit and loaded magnetic sensitivity. Corresponding incremental sensitivity indices for the isothermal case with $v_h = f(B, i_1)$ only can be defined in terms of

$$dv_h = \left(\frac{\partial v_h}{\partial B}\right)_{i_1 = k} \partial B + \left(\frac{\partial v_h}{\partial i_1}\right)_{B = k} di_1 , \tag{4.11}$$

where the partial derivatives $\partial v_h / \partial B$ and $\partial v_h / \partial i_1$ represent the incremental magnetic sensitivity and the incremental current sensitivity of Hall generators. Table 4.1 provides an example of relevant room-temperature parameters of a typical InAs Hall generator made of bulk crystalline material compared with a 10 μm thick film Hall generator.

The power output of Hall generators is a function of the ratio R_L / R_{22}. Maximum power is delivered to the load if this ratio is unity. However, this condition does not coincide with that of maximum efficiency $\eta_{max} = P_2 / P_1$, where P_1 is the power applied to the input circuit and P_2 is the power dissipated in R_L, nor does it coincide with the value of R_L required for minimizing the nonlinear dependence of v_h on B. For η_{max}, the load resistance should have [68] a value between that of R_{22} and $2R_{22}$.

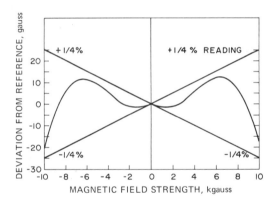

Figure 4.7. Linearity error of a Hall generator loaded by its optimum linearization load resistance (by courtesy of F. W. Bell Inc., Columbus, Ohio).

Table 4.1. An illustrative example and a comparison of a bulk crystalline InAs Hall generator with a thin film device produced by chemical vapor phase transport.

Parameters	Bulk crystalline InAs	Thin film InAs
Input resistance R_{11}	~2 ohm	20–100 ohm
Output resistance R_{22}	~1 ohm	20–100 ohm
Magnetic field sensitivity γ_B	15 mV kG^{-1}	15 mV kG^{-1}
Nominal control current i_1	150 mA	15 mA
Residual misalignment voltage v_0	~50 μV	~2 mV
$\dfrac{1}{v_h}\dfrac{dv_h}{dT}$	$-0\cdot05\%$ deg^{-1}	$-0\cdot1\%$ deg^{-1}

4.5 Noise and other perturbations

The incremental sensitivity and the secular stability of the output signals derived from Hall generators and magnetoresistors are a function of inherent noise contributions [61]. The most significant of these is thermal noise (also called Johnson noise or Nyquist noise) produced by the random motion of charge carriers in a resistor R. The mean square noise voltage $\langle v^2 \rangle$, i.e. the average value of the square of the noise voltage developed across the resistor, is $\langle v^2 \rangle = 4kTRB_W$, where k is Boltzmann's constant, T is the absolute temperature, R is the resistance of the resistor in ohms, and B_W is the bandwith of the noise in Hz. The latter depends on the properties of the detector used to measure $\langle v^2 \rangle$. In addition to thermal noise, two more noise sources are identified with current flow in semi-conductors due to random fluctuations in the charge carrier density: generation–recombination (G–R) noise, caused by a spontaneous fluctuation in the generation, recombination, and trapping statistics of charge carriers, and $1/f$ noise, so called because of its inverse frequency noise–power spectrum characteristic. The spatial distribution of the fluctuations in charge carrier density causes noise voltage perturbations in the direction of the current flow, as well as in directions at right angles to it. Fluctuations in charge carrier density produce a misalignment voltage noise between the Hall electrodes of a Hall generator in $B = 0$ at thermal equilibrium and a further noise component, defined as Hall noise, in the presence of a magnetic field. The spatial correlation of G–R noise in intrinsic Ge Hall plates was investigated theoretically and experimentally by Epstein and Brophy [263]. Their analytical model presumes that a specimen may be regarded as a combination of mutually uncorrelated elements of resistance fluctuation, and from their experimental data it appears that the size of these elements is about four times the diffusion length of excess carriers in the semiconductor. They showed that potential fluctuations at any pairs of terminals of a Hall generatore are due both to the resistance fluctuations of individual elements and to a current redistribution in the specimen which gives rise to negative coefficients of spatial correlation.

In single-crystal InSb, the misalignment noise, which has a $1/f$ dependence, does not exceed the thermal noise by an appreciable margin, and the thermal noise is uncorrelated with the misalignment and Hall noise. Spontaneous fluctuations in electron density Δn appear as fluctuations in Hall voltage Δv_h. If Δn and Δv_h have respective spectral intensities of $S_n(f)$ and $S_v(f)$, then $S_v(f) = (v_h/n)^2 S_n(f)$, so that Hall noise is essentially the $S_n(f)$ component.

Burckhardt and Strutt [62] found that, if $R_{12} = -R_{21}$, then the input and output thermal noise sources of InSb and InAs Hall generators are uncorrelated. Very low levels of G–R noise are due mainly to the short lifetimes of excess carriers in InSb and InAs. Shot noise, in intrinsic

InSb at room temperature, is about three orders of magnitude below
thermal noise [63].

The current noise in evaporated films of InSb and InAs was measured
at room temperature by Epstein [64]. The noise signals of flash-
evaporated InSb and InAs films, as well as that of InSb films evaporated
by the 'three-temperature' method were found to have a $1/f$ dependence
between 5 Hz and 10^4 Hz. The noise power is proportional to $i^{1 \cdot 6}$ for
the flash evaporated films, and to $i^{2 \cdot 1}$ for the 'three-temperature'
specimens [6]. Surface conditions play a dominant role in the generation
of $1/f$ noise; in particular, the surface-to-volume ratio affects the level
of $1/f$ noise [65]. However, the current noise in films cannot be
interpreted solely in terms of their surface-to-volume ratio. It is likely
that other factors (grain boundaries, trapping phenomena), whose effect
has not been investigated as yet, also play a significant role.

Brophy [65] also found $1/f$ noise if a temperature gradient was set up
in a homogeneous semiconductor. The absolute thermoelectric e.m.f.
per degree $d\theta_e/dT$, produced by a temperature gradient, is

$$\frac{d\theta_e}{dT} = \pm \left(\frac{\Delta\epsilon_f}{eT} + \frac{2k}{e} \right) , \qquad (4.12)$$

where $\Delta\epsilon_f$ is the energy difference between the Fermi level and the band
edge (positive sign holds for p-type material). Fluctuations in the Fermi
level show up as fluctuations in thermovoltage, an effect known as
Seebeck noise.

Other perturbations include voltages induced in the input or output
circuit due to time-varying magnetic fields [66], self-induced magnetic
fields [67], and others due to mutual inductance coupling between the
input and output circuits; these appear for time-varying high-frequency
input currents. Theoretically, this voltage is distinct from the
misalignment voltage; it is a quadrature voltage for sinusoidal input
currents, whilst the misalignment voltage is in phase with the current.
However, in practice, the stray capacitances are also significant in high
frequencies and mask the distinction between these two phenomena.

Magnetoresistors

Magnetoresistors are two-terminal devices whose resistances are nonlinear functions of the magnitude but not of the sign (direction) of an applied magnetic field. The principle on which magnetoresistors in current use are based is the galvanic or electrostatic short circuit of the Hall field. The complementarity between the Hall effect and magnetoresistance phenomena was described in earlier chapters. In Section 3.2, in particular, the geometry-dependent decrease in Hall field with a corresponding increase in $\Delta R/R_0$ was discussed in detail.

For classification purposes magnetoresistors may be placed into either of two categories: (1) devices in which a geometrical magnetoresistance $(\Delta R/R_0)_G$ is produced by choosing an appropriate size, shape, and number of metallic electrodes on a semiconducting body, and (2) magnetoresistors in which the Hall field is shorted by metallic filamentary inclusions or microscopic needles distributed anisotropically within a high-mobility semiconducting matrix. The physical magnetoresistance effect $(\Delta R/R_0)_P$ present in the semimetal bismuth [70] and in semiconductors with more than one band of charge carriers is used only rarely in present-day device applications.

A magnetoresistor configuration, in which the Hall field is constrained to zero, is the Corbino disc shown in Figure 1.2. The coaxial center and peripheral electrodes cause the current flux lines to be radial in zero magnetic field. In a magnetic field normal to the disc, the angle between the electric field $\bar{E}$ and the effective current density $\bar{J}$ in the disc is the Hall angle ϕ. The equipotential planes are concentric about the center electrode, and the current streamlines spiral outward at an angle ϕ with respect to the normals to the equipotential planes. In order to produce a high effective resistance $R(B)$ in such a disc, the inner electrode should be as small as possible; its radius r_1 should be at least $0 \cdot 1 r_2$, with r_2 the radius of the outer electrode. It is not necessary that the disc be located in a homogenous magnetic field. The major magnetic field-dependent variation in resistance takes place near the center electrode. The magnetic induction B applied to a Corbino disc may be introduced by means of focused flux concentrators; metallic cooling fins may then be applied to the outer electrodes in order to improve its dissipation of Joule heat.

Other magnetoresistor configurations geometrically analogous to a Corbino disc, such as hollow cylinders [71, 72] or truncated hollow cones with electrodes on their inner and outer surfaces, subjected to a radially symmetric magnetic field, may be described as magnetic transducers with properties similar to those of a Corbino disc.

For materials with a single conduction band of charge carriers, Equation (1.8) represents the Corbino disc magnetoresistance $(\Delta R/R_0)_C$

proportional to the square of the Hall tangent. In spite of its small bandgap and consequently its high temperature dependence, InSb is at present the most often used material for magnetoresistor applications. In the intrinsic range, the hole mobility μ_p is much smaller than the electron mobility and the electron-to-hole mobility ratio $b \gg 1$; the Corbino magnetoresistance behaves in a different manner in weak and in strong magnetic fields:

$$\left(\frac{\Delta R}{R_0}\right)_C \approx \frac{9\pi}{16}(\mu_n B)^2 \qquad \text{for } \tan\phi \leqslant 1$$

$$\left(\frac{\Delta R}{R_0}\right)_C \approx \frac{9\pi}{16}(\mu_p B)^2 + b \qquad \text{for } \tan\phi \geqslant 1$$

$$\left(\frac{\Delta R}{R_0}\right)_C \approx \frac{9\pi}{32}\mu_n \mu_p B^2 \qquad \text{for } \mu_p B \gg 1 . \qquad (5.1)$$

Thus $(\Delta R/R_0)_C$ follows a B^2 dependence in low fields, drops below the B^2 curve in higher fields, and eventually returns to a B^2 dependence in very high fields.

5.1 Raster plates and raster pattern magnetoresistors
In Section 3.2 it was shown that the magnetoresistance of a rectangular plate whose length-to-width ratio is small approaches $(\Delta R/R_0)_C$ in the limit of $w/l \to \infty$. This effect is brought about by its current electrodes which short-circuit electrostatically the transverse Hall field. This geometry dependence was demonstrated by Weiss and Welker [73] on InSb plates; more than one order-of-magnitude increase in resistance over its zero field value $R(0)$ can be obtained in 10 kG on a $0 \cdot 5$ mm thick plate whose major surfaces (10×3 mm) are covered by metallic electrodes. In view of the room temperature conductivity of InSb, $\sigma \approx 2 \times 10^2$ ohm^{-1} cm^{-1}, the resistance $R(B)$ of such a plate is too small (less than 1 ohm) for practical applications. A larger resistance may be obtained from a series-connected array of such plates stacked upon each other; the effective magnetoresistance $(\Delta R/R_0)_G$ is essentially the same as that of a single plate. A somewhat smaller $(\Delta R/R_0)$ can be obtained by vacuum-depositing or electroplating a raster of metallic lines [74, 75] on an InSb plate in such a manner that the InSb strips included between these lines have a small length-to-width (l/w) ratio in the direction of the input current.

InSb film raster pattern magnetoresistors [76] can be produced by vacuum-depositing $0 \cdot 5$ to 2 μm thick In films onto the surface of high mobility ($\mu_n > 5 \times 10^4$ cm^2 V^{-1} s^{-1}) electron beam zone crystallized InSb films, 2 to 5 μm in thickness, on glass substrates. Photolithographic procedures are then employed to etch out an indium line raster pattern upon the InSb films similar to that shown in Figure 5.1 (p.54ff.). They can be made with $R(0)$ values from a few ohms to several thousand ohms. The

$(\Delta R/R_0)_G$ of such a magnetoresistor is proportional to B^2 up to ~2 kG and is linear in B above ~3 kG; it increases with μ_n and with the increasing density of the In lines, i.e. with a decrease in the l/w ratio of the InSb stripes included between them.

Considering a film raster plate of thickness d, in a Cartesian coordinate system, the indium electrodes are in the (x, y) plane, parallel to the InSb film surfaces. The dimensions l and w are taken along the x and y axes and refer, respectively, to the length and width of the In electrodes as well as to the InSb regions enclosed between them. In zero magnetic field the current flows along the x axis. The current density vector has J_x as well as J_y and J_z components. The electric field distribution in the presence of a magnetic field is

$$\frac{\partial^2 V}{\partial x^2} + \frac{\partial^2 V}{\partial y^2} + (1 + \tan^2 \phi)\frac{\partial^2 V}{\partial z^2} = 0 \ . \tag{5.2}$$

A charge density σ_c is present such that

$$\sigma_c = \tan^2 \phi \frac{\partial^2 V}{\partial z^2}\frac{1}{4\pi} \ . \tag{5.3}$$

Only if $\sigma_c = 0$ is the two-dimensional solution [Equation (3.18)] of Laplace's equation applicable.

A resistance-paper analog plot, shown in Figure 5.2, was made of the potential distribution along the cross section of an electrode simulating the condition in a raster plate in the vicinity of an electrode. The results indicate that only for distances from the electrodes of $\Delta x < d$ are the equipotentials a function of z, For $\Delta x > d$ the current streamlines and equipotentials behave as though the (y, z) planes under the In electrodes were effectively equipotential surfaces, so that the two-dimensional solution of Laplace's equation is applicable in the fractional film volume $1 - \epsilon$, where $\epsilon \approx 2d/l$. High raster line densities are desirable in order to decrease the l/w ratio, and thus to increase the magnetic field sensitivity $\partial(\Delta R/R_0)\partial B$ of magnetoresistors, as well as for increasing their effective resistance per unit surface area. A raster consisting of 1 μm In lines is well within the resolution attainable at the present time by means of standard photolithographic techniques. However, the distortion of the

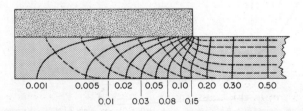

| 0.001 | 0.005 | 0.02 | 0.05 | 0.10 | 0.20 | 0.30 | 0.50 |

| 0.01 | 0.03 | 0.08 | 0.15 |

Figure 5.2. Analog plot made on resistance paper showing current streamlines and equipotentials in a film in the vicinity of a metallic current electrode.

equipotential lines is likely to be significant and might lead to a
reduction in $\Delta R/R_0$ unless the film thickness d is also reduced. A
reduction in film thickness to less than 3 μm does not appear desirable,
because μ_n decreases with decreasing d owing to surface scattering of
electrons.

5.2 Indium antimonide–nickel antimonide field plates
Some of the properties of the pseudobinary eutectic alloy InSb–NiSb were
described in Section 2.5. Preferentially oriented NiSb needles, ~50 μm
in length and less than 1 μm in diameter, with a room temperature
conductivity $\sigma = 10^4$ ohm^{-1} cm^{-1}, short-circuit the Hall field generated
in the InSb matrix ($\sigma \approx 2 \times 10^2$ ohm^{-1} cm^{-1}) in which the needles are
embedded. A large transverse magnetoresistance [77] results if the
current density vector, the needle axes, and the magnetic induction are
mutually orthogonal; $(\Delta R/R_0)_G$ is about half that expected for a perfect
short circuit of the Hall field. This is reasonable in view of the fact that
the l/w ratio of the InSb segment between the needles is not infinitesimal
and the conductivity of the needles is not infinite. Typical curves are
shown in Figure 5.3.

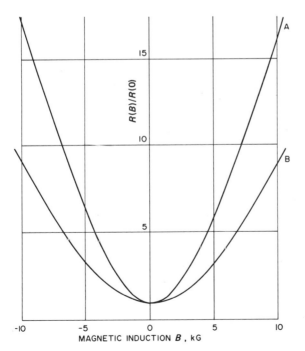

Figure 5.3. Relative resistance $R(B)/R(0)$ as a function of magnetic induction B of
magnetoresistor field plates; curve A, intrinsic InSb–NiSb eutectic material;
curve B, Te-doped InSb–NiSb (after Weiss, H., Wilhelm, M., 1963, Z. Phys., **176**, 399).

Field plates can be produced by photolithographic procedures, in meander-shaped configurations, to provide $R(0)$ values between 10 and 500 ohm. Field plates, having the needle axes parallel to the plate, may be reduced to ~20 μm in thickness; they are fragile and must be attached for support to insulating ceramic substrates. Surface densities of resistance up to 300 ohm mm^{-2} (for $B = 0$) can be obtained in this manner. If the axes of the needles are normal to the plate, then its thickness must be at least 60 μm so that the separation between the needles should be sufficiently small in comparison with their length, otherwise the magnetoresistance decreases.

The temperature dependence of the relative resistance [78] $R(B)/R(0)$ of intrinsic InSb–NiSb is shown in Figure 5.4 for three specific temperatures: room temperature, the temperature of liquid nitrogen, and that of liquid helium, respectively. The maximum magnetoresistance is obtained, evidently, at −196°C, where lattice scattering is much smaller than at 20°C, but impurity scattering is still negligible. At −269°C the electrons are subjected to strong impurity scattering. This reduces their

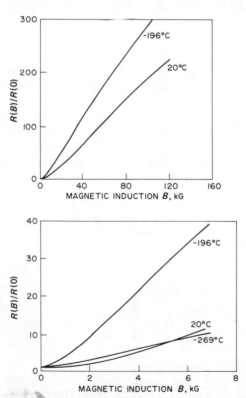

Figure 5.4. Relative resistance $R(B)/R(0)$ of eutectic InSb–NiSb field plate as a function of magnetic induction and temperature (after Weiss [78]).

mobility, and the magnetic field dependence of the magnetoresistance is analogous to its room temperature values.

Doping the eutectic alloy with donor impurities causes an increase in the conductivity of the InSb matrix. This reduces the temperature dependence of the magnetoresistance, but causes a decrease in $\Delta R/R_0$, partly because of the decrease in μ_n with n and partly because of the increase of the conductivity of the InSb matrix with respect to that of the needles.

5.3 Thin film magnetoresistors

The magnetoresistance of dendritic InSb + In films (mentioned in Section 2.5) grown from liquid, previously vacuum-codeposited layers of In and Sb films is smaller than that of bulk crystalline InSb + NiSb. This is due in part to the fact that μ_n of InSb dendrites is smaller than that of bulk InSb. It is also due to the imperfectly ordered In filaments within the InSb matrix, a consequence of the rapid solidification procedure used to grow the nonstoichiometric liquid films. There are, nevertheless, a number of advantages to be claimed for thin film magnetoresistors. One of these is their relatively high surface density of resistance. A high resistance per unit surface area is desirable in order to obtain a high magnetic induction by focusing a given magnetic flux over a small surface area. Furthermore, thin film magnetoresistors can be processed into complex shapes on either plane or curved substrates. They can also be produced in noninductive configurations such as required for high-frequency applications. Films grown on corundum substrates, less than 1 μm in thickness, dissipate heat efficiently because of their large surface-to-volume ratio and the high thermal conductance of corundum.

Films in which the dendrites are oriented at random with respect to each other have a magnetoresistance which has only a slight dependence on macroscopic geometrical factors. It is feasible, however, to produce two-phase (InSb + In) films in which the dendrites are essentially parallel and connected to each other by narrow segments of In segregated out of the dendrites during their lateral expansion and growth. A magnetoresistor configuration produced from such a material is shown in Figure 5.5 (p.54ff.), and Figure 5.6 shows that its magnetoresistance is a quadratic function of B below 3 kG and a linear function of B in higher magnetic fields, with a slope $(1/R_0)(dR/dB) = (7\cdot8 \pm 0\cdot1) \times 10^{-4}\,\mathrm{G}^{-1}$.

The physical magnetoresistance $(\Delta R/R_0)_P$ of bulk crystalline bismuth [79, 80], although small at 295°K, reaches a value $(\Delta R/R_0)_P \approx 21$ at 77°K in $B = 10$ kG. Thin film Bi magnetoresistors of arbitrary geometry can be produced by electroplating Bi, from a BiCl$_3$ solution in aqueous HCl, onto a photolithographically-prepared base pattern of Cu on an insulating substrate. After an ~10 μm thick Bi film [81] is plated onto the base pattern and a protective plastic overlayer coated onto it, the Cu base is dissolved, thus freeing the magnetoresistor from its insulating substrate. Contact to the electrode tabs of the magnetoresistor are made by attaching gold wire leads using adhesive silver paint. For an $R(0) = 360$ ohm, a $\Delta R/R_0 = 15$ was obtained at $77°K$ for $B = 10$ kG. Bi film magnetoresistors have potentially useful applications at cryogenic temperatures as control elements and magnetic transducers.

Miniature bismuth magnetoresistors, about $20 \ \mu m \times 15 \ \mu m$ in size, for use at cryogenic temperatures, have been developed by Shiffman [82]. The process consists in drawing a microscopic boule from a bismuth melt at the tip of a $20 \ \mu m$ (diameter) 50% Cu–Au wire bent into a V-shape; a second V is attached to the other end of the boule, which solidifies in the form of a single-crystal cylinder. The Bi trigonal axis is usually aligned normal to the length of the cylinder. Subsequent melting and recrystallization realigns the trigonal axis with the axis of the cylinder. This leads to a quadratic field dependence of the magnetoresistance, $(\Delta R/R_0)_P \approx kB^2$, for $B \leqslant 0·8$ kG; k is between 2×10^{-6} and $3 \times 10^{-6} \ G^{-2}$ at $77°K$, and in the liquid helium range k values are between 10^{-5} and $1·5 \times 10^{-6} \ G^{-2}$. However, the resistance is a linear function of T and, near $77°K$, k is inversely proportional to the resistivity.

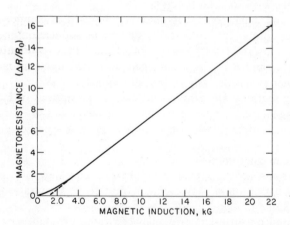

Figure 5.6. Room temperature magnetoresistance as a function of magnetic induction of representative InSb + In film magnetoresistor.

Applications of Hall generators and magnetoresistors

Practical applications of Hall generators and magnetoresistors include sensory functions, such as provided by magnetic flux transducers, as well as analog signal processing operations, for example modulation and detection. The cross interaction between electric and magnetic fields inherent in galvanomagnetic phenomena leads to these, as well as to a large number of related electronic circuit applications.

Generically, Hall generators and magnetoresistors may be considered as magnetic transducers; they translate the input variable, the vector magnitude of the magnetic induction, into a corresponding electrical output signal. The linearity inherent in properly loaded Hall generators leads, logically, to the use of such devices for field probes and magnetometers, for measuring and mapping the distribution of magnetic fields. Magneto-resistors, in spite of their nonlinear $R(B)$ versus B dependence, can be used for the same purposes. They can be used in linked electrical and magnetic bridge circuits for sensing an imbalance of magnetic fluxes, as high-resolution noncontacting potentiometers, proximity switches, as well as linear and angular position transducers.

Hall generators and magnetoresistors may also be used as components of analog or digital computers: operations such as multiplication and division, squaring, and taking the square root of quantities represented by the input variables i_1 and B can be performed over wide dynamic ranges, at high speeds either synchronously or asynchronously.

In the following sections, the circuit and device applications of Hall generators and magnetoresistors are described in general and listed in related categories, including illustrative examples of their specific uses.

6.1 Hall generator magnetometers

One of the earliest and most important applications considered for Hall generators is the detection and measurement of static or time-varying magnetic fields. Some of their advantages in comparison with magnetometers based on different principles [83] are: (1) Hall generators are mechanically static devices, unlike rotating-coil gaussmeters, which measure the time derivative of a magnetic field; (2) Hall generators occupy a small volume and do not perturb the magnetic field to be measured to any significant extent; (3) Hall generators can be used in high magnetic field gradients, unlike nuclear precession resonance magnetometers; (4) their frequency response is higher than that of most magnetometers; they can be used to measure transient and synchronously-pulsed magnetic fields. However, they are nonlinear in B, they have a high temperature sensitivity, and a large thermal time constant.

For magnetometer applications, Hall generators with the following properties are required: (a) the null point (i.e. the output voltage across the

Hall terminals in $B = 0$) should be independent of time and temperature; (b) the Hall voltage in $B \neq 0$ and the magnetic sensitivity γ_B should be large and as nearly temperature-independent as possible; (c) the Hall voltage should be a linear function of the magnetic induction. Of these three conditions, the first is the more fundamental because the other two, which involve an admixture of magnetoresistance and Hall effect, causing a nonlinear v_h versus B dependence and a temperature dependence due to variations in the ambient temperature and Joule heat, can be compensated by auxiliary circuitry and thermal shielding. However, fluctuations in the null point determine the lower limit of a detectable magnetic induction B_{min}, as well as the resolution of Hall generators in higher magnetic fields. Thermal noise in Hall generators is two to three orders of magnitude greater than flicker or shot noise (Section 4.5), particularly in n-type III–V compound semiconductors. The mean square thermal noise power is $P_n = kTB_w$, where B_w is the bandwidth of the detector used to measure the noise fluctuations. The output power P_o delivered by a Hall generator to a load $R_L = R_{22}$, matched for maximum power transfer, is $P_o = P_i(\mu_n B/4)^2$, where P_i is the power supplied by the input current; therefore

$$B_{min} = \frac{4}{\mu_n}\left(\frac{P_o}{P_i}\right)^{\frac{1}{2}}.$$

(6.1)

At the null point $P_o = P_n$; consequently,

$$B_{min} = \frac{4}{\mu_n}\left(\frac{kTB_w}{P_i}\right)^{\frac{1}{2}}.$$

(6.2)

Equation (6.2) states that the threshold of detection can be lowered by choosing a material with a higher electron mobility and by decreasing the bandwidth of the Hall output detector. Using an alternating magnetic field, a detector with a bandwidth of 2 Hz, and an InAs Hall generator, Weiss [84] determined, by means of Equation (6.2), a value $B_{min} \approx 6 \times 10^{-6}$ G. For a static or time-varying magnetic field (below 1 Hz) $B_{min} \approx 10^{-4}$ G, and is determined not by the noise but by the localized thermal fluctuations of the Hall generator due to the imperfect heat transfer and heat exchange with its surroundings.

The simplest Hall magnetometers employ Hall generators driven by a d.c. current source regulated to better than 1%. The output electrodes are connected to an appropriate load resistance R_L, which determines the operational range for a nominal v_h versus B linearity. A potentiometric measurement of v_h is then compared against a previously calibrated scale. At room temperature, accuracies of the order of 1% of full-scale value can be obtained in this manner. Thermostatically-controlled Hall plates of InAs ($R_h \approx -100$ cm^3 C^{-1} and temperature coefficient of $\sim 10^{-3}$ deg^{-1}) can be used for the measurement of magnetic inductions greater than ~ 1 kG to within an error of 10^{-4}. Hall generators of InAs$_{0.8}$P$_{0.2}$, which have a lower γ_B than InAs but also a smaller temperature dependence, were shown by Mulady [85] to have a resolution of 0·001% (calibrated against a nuclear magnetic resonance probe), provided that they were maintained within an enclosure where the temperature was maintained to within 0·1 deg. The proportionality between the magnetic induction and the Hall output voltage is a function of geometrical factors of the Hall plate and of the load resistor connected across the Hall electrodes. This proportionality may be tested against an inherently linear magnetometer such as the rotating-coil gaussmeter, and the instrument may be calibrated in terms of a nuclear precession resonance magnetometer, whose inherent error is within 10^{-5} to 10^{-6} (in homogenous magnetic fields).

Hall generators driven by sinusoidally alternating current sources provide a number of advantages for magnetometers: (1) a reduction in $1/f$ noise (Section 4.5) can be obtained by the use of audio frequencies; (2) a reduction in the bandwidth of the Hall output voltage detector is feasible by the use of simple circuits and components; (3) there is an elimination of thermoelectric error voltages; (4) there is noise cancellation by means of synchronous detection schemes. The last method, in particular, affords a considerable improvement in performance of Hall effect magnetometers. Disadvantages of using a.c. input currents include inductive coupling errors and cross coupling between input and output circuits of Hall generators.

A magnetometer [86], which illustrates the advantages to be derived from the a.c. coupled Hall generators, is shown in the form of a block diagram in Figure 6.1. It has a resolution of 0·01% and covers in 12 full scales the ranges from 0·1 G to 30 kG. A $1·1 \times 10^3$ Hz oscillator provides the 100 mA input current applied to the Hall plate. The Hall output voltage results from the amplitude modulation of this current

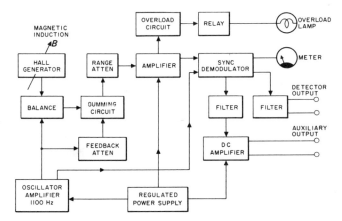

Figure 6.1. Block diagram of an incremental gaussmeter employing an a.c. driven Hall generator for measuring magnetic fields (by courtesy of F. W. Bell Inc., Columbus, Ohio).

by the magnetic field to be measured due to the inherent multiplying action of the Hall effect. A fraction of the oscillator output is fed back to a summing circuit in reverse phase. Control of amplitude and phase allows the cancellation of the major fraction of the signal caused by the magnetic field. This allows the amplifier gain to be increased, up to two orders in magnitude; the resultant scale expansion permits small changes in magnetic field to be studied in detail. After amplification, the signal is demodulated in order to obtain a d.c. or lower frequency a.c. signal proportional to the magnetic field. The synchronous detector rejects any out-of-phase signal components; in-phase components are the only ones containing incremental signal information. Furthermore, it rejects all signals except those derived from the $1 \cdot 1 \times 10^3$ Hz carrier frequency. The detector output reverses polarity, with reversal in direction of B; this causes a phase-reversed signal in the amplifier, and in this manner the information on the sense of B is retained in the output.

The effective sensitivity of a Hall generator can be increased considerably by mounting it between high-permeability magnetic flux concentrators, as shown by Ross $et\ al.$ [87]. The flux concentrators tend to focus the flux upon the Hall generator. The gain in sensitivity increases, to a first-order approximation, linearly with the length of cylindrical concentrators (10 to 30 cm in length), provided that their cross section is uniform and covers the effective surface of the Hall generator. Hieronymus and Weiss [88] have determined the gain in sensitivity as a function of the permeability, length-to-diameter ratio of cylindrical rods and the spacing between them. Using μ-metal rods, 20 cm long and $1 \cdot 1$ cm in diameter, with a Hall generator placed between them in a gap of $0 \cdot 03$ cm, they obtained a gain of ~400; without the flux concentrators they found $B_{min} \approx 2 \times 10^{-3}$ G, and with the same Hall generator mounted between the flux concentrators B_{min} dropped to 5×10^{-6} G, Analytical expressions for the optimum size and shape of flux concentrators were calculated by Warmuth [89] and Epstein and Schulz [90] in terms of demagnetization factors and magnetic permeability. Flux collectors of μ-metal or ferrite also cause a distortion of the magnetic field in their immediate vicinity[1]. However, at a distance from the sensor equal to the length of the flux concentrators, the distortion of the magnetic field does not exceed 6%.

A simple portable magnetometer suitable for measuring anomalies in the Earth's magnetic field, adequate for archaeological explorations, was described by Owston [91]. It is shown schematically in Figure 6.2. Without the temperature-control system and with the Hall generator cemented to the flux concentrators, the magnetometer had a noise level equivalent to ~2×10^{-5} G and a large drift, of thermal origin, ~10^{-3} G min^{-1}. With the temperature controller in operation, the

---

[1] A method of reducing this perturbation by the use of feedback and a specially shaped magnetic field has been suggested by Milligan and Burgess [92].

instrument was found to have a resolution of 5×10^{-5} G. This corresponds to an angular error in positioning of the flux concentrators of $\sim 0 \cdot 75°$. If the magnetometer is rotated in a horizontal plane then, as the flux concentrators pass through the magnetic meridian, the meter reading is a maximum. If the magnetometer is then rotated in the plane of the magnetic meridian, the meter reads a maximum when the flux concentrators lie along the direction of an anomaly in the Earth's magnetic field. By rotating the bar magnet, the meter reading is brought to zero at one location. The magnetometer is then brought to another site and again aligned in the direction of the anomaly. The meter reading indicates the difference in the total intensity of the Earth's field between the two locations. An advantage of such a device over the more precise nuclear magnetic resonance probe is its ability to perform well in the presence of large magnetic field gradients.

A solid-state compass employing Hall effect magnetometers was described by Keller [93]. It is shown schematically in Figure 6.3. Two flux-concentrator-equipped Hall generators, disposed at 90° with respect to each other, are used to determine the azimuthal angle θ between the flux concentrators and the horizontal component of the Earth's magnetic field. The Hall generators are driven by a two-phase sinusoidal oscillator with an output frequency of $2 \cdot 5$ to 5 kHz. One of the two Hall generators is driven directly and the other by a current shifted in phase by $\frac{1}{2}\pi$. The components of the Earth's magnetic field,

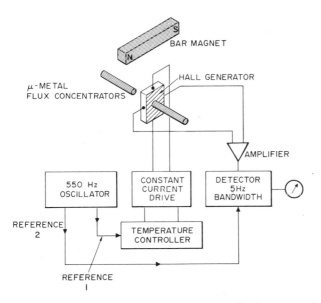

Figure 6.2. A portable magnetometer suitable for detecting and measuring anomalies in the Earth's magnetic field (after Owston [91]).

in the horizontal plane, are $B_0 \cos\theta$ and $B_0 \sin\theta$; the input currents to the Hall generators are, respectively, $i_1 = i_0 \cos\omega t$ and $i' = i_0 \sin\omega t$. The two output voltages are added algebraically; they can be written as

$$v_{h1} = \frac{R_h}{d} B_0 i_0 \cos\omega t \cos\theta$$

$$v_{h2} = \frac{R_h}{d} B_0 i_0 \sin\omega t \sin\theta . \tag{6.3}$$

Their resultant $v_h = v_{h1} + v_{h2}$ is then

$$v_h = k \cos(\omega t + \theta) , \tag{6.4}$$

where $k = (R_h/d) B_0 i_0$; a reference signal derived directly from the oscillator drives a Schmitt trigger circuit which, as the sinusoidal input voltage passes through a predetermined level in each cycle, produces an output pulse which sets the bistable flip-flop, shown in Figure 6.3. The summed Hall output signal v_h drives a second trigger circuit which resets the flip-flop. The duration (but not the amplitude) of the output pulses from the flip-flop are thus phase-modulated by the angle θ. These pulses are then applied to an integrating amplifier whose output voltage v_0 is a linear function of θ, as shown in Figure 6.3. Such a compass, designed for hydrographic investigations, was found to have a resolution of $\pm1°$ of arc and a response time to angular changes of $\sim10^{-3}$ s.

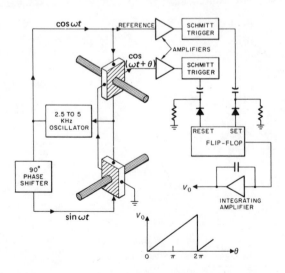

Figure 6.3. Hall-effect compass employing flux-concentrator-equipped Hall generator; the compass is used for determining the azimuthal angle θ between the flux concentrator axis and the horizontal component of the Earth's magnetic field (after Keller [93]).

6.2 Magnetoresistance-based magnetometers

Magnetoresistors, in spite of their nonlinear dependence on the magnetic induction, can be used as sensitive magnetometers or component elements of a solid-state compass. Epstein *et al.* [94] have described such a device employing InSb or InAs Corbino discs mounted in the gap between ferromagnetic flux concentrators. The flux-dependent response of a Corbino disc is linearized by the application of a large, steady-state magnetic biasing field B_0. Let the resistance of the disc $R(B_0)_c = R(0)[1 + \mu_n^2 B_0^2]$. If the small field to be measured B_x is superposed on B_0, then the effective resistance $R_c(B_0 + B_x)$ can be obtained by a Taylor series expansion about B_0, with $f(B) = \mu_n^2 B^2$:

$$R_c(B_0 + B_x) = R(B_0) + R(0)\left[\frac{\partial f(B)}{\partial B}B_x + \frac{1}{2}\frac{\partial^2 f(B)}{\partial B^2}B_x^2 + \frac{1}{n!}\frac{\partial^n f(B)}{\partial B^n}B_x^n \cdots \right]. \tag{6.5}$$

The change in resistance due to B_x is $\Delta R_c = R(B_0 + B_x) - R(B_0)$ and the function $f(B)$ has no derivative beyond the second; therefore

$$\frac{\Delta R_c}{R(0)} = \mu_n^2(B_x^2 + 2B_0 B_x) \approx 2\mu_n^2 B_0 B_x \qquad \text{for } B_x \ll 2B_0 . \tag{6.6}$$

The change in resistance is essentially proportional to B_x in small magnetic fields. This is the basis for an incrementally linear magnetoresistance magnetometer.

The flux concentrators must be made of a material which retains its large incremental permeability in the presence of B_0 in order to obtain an effective flux gain in the gap between them. Nearly all magnetic materials have their highest incremental permeability at $B = 0$, and the permeability decreases with B; the lower the saturation magnetization, the stronger is the reduction in permeability. The reason for using an alloy such as 'silectron' (silicon steel) is its high magnetic saturation and relatively high incremental permeability, even at $B \geqslant 5$ kG. For B_0, Epstein *et al.* used an 'Alnico V' permanent magnet [(2)] shunting the flux concentrators, which provided an initial flux gain of ~70; the sensitivity of their magnetometer was ~8 mV G^{-1}.

A considerably larger sensitivity, as well as high stability, can be achieved by driving magnetoresistance-based magnetometers with a time-varying periodic magnetic biasing field, as shown by von Borcke *et al.* [95]. Because of the symmetry of the $R(B)$ versus B curve about $B = 0$, the effective value of the resistance is proportional to $\sin^2 \omega t$, where ω is the angular frequency of the magnetic excitation $B(\omega)$. If a small steady-state magnetic field B_x is superposed on $B(\omega)$, then the inherent symmetry of response of the magnetoresistor is removed, producing a change in resistance ΔR, which varies at the frequency ω of the alternating bias

---

[(2)] Alnico V has a relatively low magnetic permeability of ~3 and does not cause a magnetic short circuit of the gap between the high-permeability flux concentrators.

$B(\omega)$. This is illustrated schematically for a trapezoidal driving field in Figure 6.4.

The principal element of the magnetoresistance magnetometer is the bridge circuit shown in Figure 6.5a. The center-tapped transformer provides the input current $i = i_0 \cos \omega t$ for the identical magnetoresistors R_1 and R_2. It also provides the magnetizing current for the two identical solenoids L_1 and L_2 which generate the magnetic inductions acting on the respective magnetoresistors. If their inductive reactances are large with respect to their ohmic resistances, then the magnetic fields $B_0 \sin \omega t$ are in quadrature with respect to i. In terms of Figure 6.4,

$$R(B)_1 = R(0) + k(B_x + B_0 \sin \omega t)^2$$

$$R(B)_2 = R(0) + k(-B_x + B_0 \sin \omega t)^2 , \qquad (6.7)$$

where the harmonics generated by the nonlinear $R(B)$ dependence are neglected and k is a coefficient which depends on the material parameters of $R(B)$. The output signal generated across the bridge circuit $\Delta v = i[R(B)_1 - R(B)_2]$ is

$$\Delta v = 2 k i_0 B_x B_0 \sin 2 \omega t . \qquad (6.8)$$

It is linearly proportional to B_x and the bridge sensitivity depends on the operating point B_0 of the $R(B)$ versus B curves (Figure 6.4). An implementation of the bridge circuit is represented by Figure 6.5b.

Flux concentrators of μ-metal, $0 \cdot 6$ cm in diameter, are used to focus the Earth's magnetic field (or that of the field to be measured) onto the magnetoresistors mounted on cylindrical ($\sim 0 \cdot 1$ cm diameter) protrusions from the face of one of the flux concentrators. The solenoids L_1 and L_2 are mounted on twin cylindrical bars emerging from the face of the opposite flux concentrator. Variations in gap width are of little significance as long as the magnetic inductions acting on both magnetoresistors change in an identical manner. The a.c. biasing fields acting on the magnetoresistors are ~ 3 kG at the input frequency of 1 kHz, as shown in Figure 6.5a. The magnetoresistor bridge output signal of 2 kHz [Equation (6.8)] is applied to a narrow-band 2 kHz differential amplifier, and its output is applied, in turn, to a synchronous detector whose reference signal is derived from the 1 kHz input by way of a frequency doubler. Using field-plate magnetoresistors, von Borcke et al. [95] obtained a sensitivity of 30 mv G^{-1} from bridge circuits (without amplification) with an input power of $1 \cdot 5$ mW per field plate. A distinguishing feature of such magnetometers is the excellent stability of their null points; between $\sim -20°C$ and $+60°C$, the fluctuations correspond to less than $0 \cdot 18$ mG.

A solid-state compass can be assembled from two magnetoresistance magnetometers oriented at right angles to each other, in analogy with the circuit shown in Figure 6.3. The input currents are chosen to be equal in amplitude but displaced in phase by $\frac{1}{2}\pi$. Defining the horizontal components of the Earth's magnetic field as $B_e \sin \theta$ and $B_e \cos \theta$

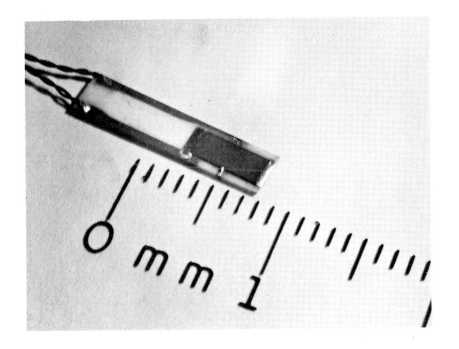

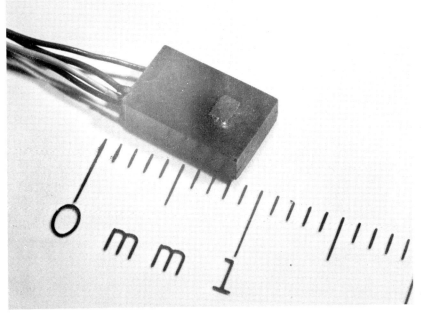

Figure 4.1. A partly assembled bulk crystalline InAs Hall generator; Hall plate on ceramic wafer support with leads attached to current and Hall electrodes; also shown is an encapsulated Hall generator (by courtesy of F. W. Bell Inc., Columbus, Ohio).

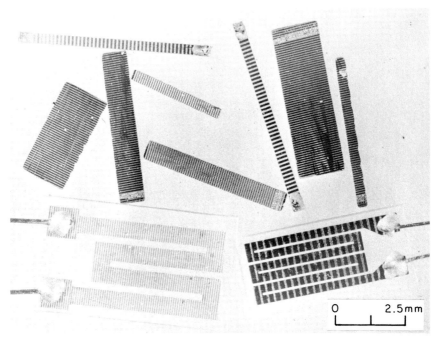

Figure 5.1. Magnetoresistors made by photolithographic procedures from electron beam microzone-crystallized InSb films on glass substrates; raster pattern consists of superposed In or Cu lines on surface of films.

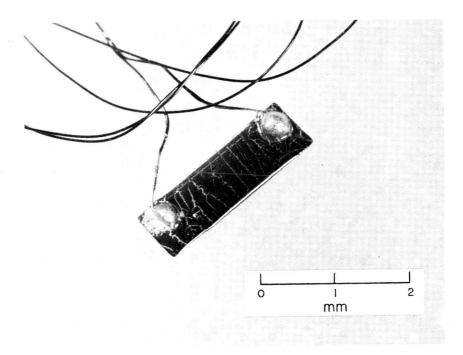

Figure 5.5. InSb + In film magnetoresistor grown by recrystallization of nonstoichiometric liquid film; light lines represent In filaments included between InSb dendrites.

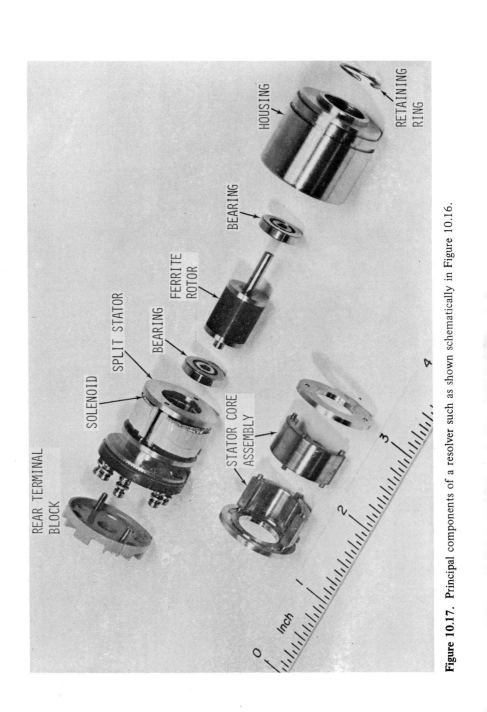

Figure 10.17. Principal components of a resolver such as shown schematically in Figure 10.16.

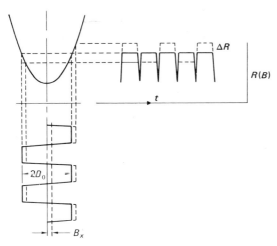

Figure 6.4. Modulation of the resistance of a magnetoresistor with a quadratic $R(B)$ dependence by a periodic magnetic induction B and a superposed steady magnetic induction B_x (after von Borcke *et al.* [95]).

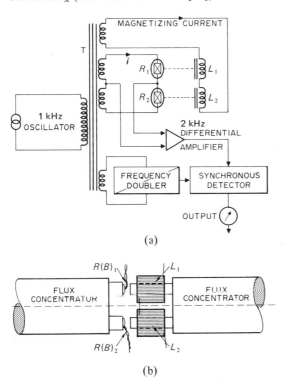

(a)

(b)

Figure 6.5. Magnetoresistance-based magnetometer: (a) block diagram of magnetometer and auxiliary circuits; (b) position of magnetoresistors $R(B)$, solenoids L_1 and L_2, and flux concentrators (after von Borcke *et al.* [95]).

respectively, we can write Equation (6.8) for the two bridge circuits in the form

$$\Delta v_1 = K \sin\theta \sin 2\omega t$$

$$\Delta v_2 = K \cos\theta \cos 2\omega t , \qquad (6.9)$$

where $K = 2ki_0 B_0 B_e$. The respective bridge output signals are applied to a linear summing amplifier and then to a phase comparator, such as shown in Figure 6.3, which produces an output voltage proportional to the azimuthal angle θ.

6.3 Magnetization, magnetic hysteresis, and flux mapping

Hall generators and magnetoresistors lend themselves to the measurement of fields generated by a residual or induced magnetization and for investigating the dynamic processes involved in magnetic hysteresis and flux reversal.

Consider a uniformly magnetized sphere whose magnetic dipole moment M is induced by the applied homogenous magnetic field H_0, shown in Figure 6.6. In cylindrical coordinates the dipole fields[3] (in a plane containing the magnetic dipole) are

$$H_r = 2M\cos\frac{\theta}{r^3} \qquad H_\theta = M\sin\frac{\theta}{r^3} . \qquad (6.10)$$

A Hall generator or magnetoresistor detects only the component H_z normal to the device. From Figure 6.6,

$$H_z = 2M\cos\theta \sin\frac{\theta}{r^3} + M\sin\theta \cos\frac{\theta}{r^3} . \qquad (6.11)$$

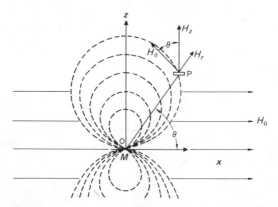

Figure 6.6. Dipole magnetic field components H_θ and H_r due to a specimen with magnetic moment M, induced by a steady uniform magnetic field H_0; H_z is the vector sum of magnetic field components normal to Hall probe P.

[3] For nonspherical specimens, the dipole field is an approximation valid at distances considerably greater than the specimen dimensions (see also Stoner, E. C., 1945, *Phil. Mag.*, **36**, 803).

For $r = x/\cos\theta$, Equation (6.11) yields

$$H_z = \frac{3M}{x^3}\cos^4\theta\sin\theta \tag{6.12}$$

and the maximum value of H_z is obtained from

$$\frac{\partial H_z}{\partial \theta} = 0 = \frac{3M}{x^3}(\cos^5\theta - 4\cos^3\theta\sin^2\theta)$$

$$\tan\theta = \frac{z}{x} = 0 \cdot 5 \ . \tag{6.13}$$

Consequently, the maximum field acting on a galvanomagnetic probe is at a height equal to half the distance from the dipole [96]. From Equation (6.12) the proportionality between H_z and M allows a direct determination of the magnetic moment per unit volume M/v.

An experimental verification of Equation (6.13) was made by Craik [96] on a small (64 mg) sphere of annealed nickel. He also demonstrated that the method is not confined to spherical specimens. Tests carried out on a rectangular cobalt crystal ($1 \cdot 0$ cm x $0 \cdot 4$ cm x $0 \cdot 3$ cm), whose easy axis of magnetization was oriented along its long dimension, indicated that, at a distance of $\sim 2 \cdot 5$ cm, the field configuration corresponded to the dipole calculations. Measurements of H_z versus H_0 were feasible at positions closer to the specimen, even touching one end of the specimen, with the data in close agreement with those obtained for $x \geqslant 10$ cm.

The absolute value of the magnetization can be inferred from the magnitude of H_z. However, the exact position of the magnetic (point) dipole must be known accurately and the displacement x must be determined with precision. Since H_z is a maximum for $z = 0 \cdot 5x$, $\cos\theta = 2/\sqrt{5}$, which, if introduced in Equation (6.12), leads to

$$(H_z)_{max} \approx 0 \cdot 8586\frac{M}{x^3} \ . \tag{6.14}$$

Therefore M can be calculated from the slope of plots of $(H_z)_{max}$ against $1/x^3$. If the plots are nonlinear, then the origin of x must be adjusted accordingly. Accuracies of 2% were obtained by Craik [96] who measured, in this manner, the magnetization of europium orthoferrite crystals.

A differential Hall generator magnetometer for measuring the saturation magnetization of spherical or cylindrical specimens was described by Vlehmann [97]. The apparatus consists of two identical Hall generators fed from different current sources immersed in a steady-state magnetic field, such as that produced by an iron core electromagnet. The output electrodes of the two Hall generators are connected in series opposition, and the combined output, applied to a balanced amplifier, is adjusted for a null. With the specimen to be measured, mounted in front of and in close proximity to one of the Hall generators, an additional dipole field $\Delta H = KMa^3/x^3$, where K is a constant of proportionality (determined by calibration), a is the radius of the specimen, and x is the distance between the sample and the Hall generator, producing a signal in the amplifier. Using a nickel sample of known magnetization as a calibration source measured with an instrument sensitivity of $10\ \mu V\ G^{-1}\ cm^{-3}$, Viehmann resolved magnetic moments of $\sim$20 G cm^{-3} with an accuracy of 1%.

An instrument for recording dynamic B versus H hysteresis loops of thin magnetic films was described by Berkowitz and Schippert [98]. Helmholtz coils are used to produce the driving field H, and a Hall generator is used to measure the normal component of the magnetic induction along an edge of the film. A signal proportional to H is used to drive one of the input ports of an XY recorder, and the output signal from a Hall generator used to measure the normal component of the magnetic induction is applied to the other input port. The recorder displays dynamic B versus H hysteresis loops, such as shown in Figure 6.7.

Other parameters, such as the intrinsic coercivity [4] H_{ci} of magnetized

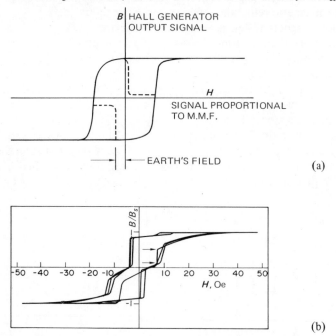

(a)

(b)

Figure 6.7. Display and measurement of magnetic hysteresis loops: (a) magnetic induction (in the plane of the film) as a function of magnetomotive force applied to a permalloy film; (b) magnetization hysteresis curves of a crystal of europium orthoferrite showing domain nucleation and motion in applied and demagnetizing fields.

[4] The demagnetizing field required for reducing the total magnetic induction B of a magnet to zero is the coercive force H_c. It is a function of its shape. The intrinsic coercive force H_{ci} is the field required for reducing the intrinsic induction $I_M = B - H$ to zero.

ferromagnetic structures [99] may be determined by means of Hall generators or magnetoresistor probes. For materials with a nearly rectangular hysteresis loop, such as Alnico V, the magnet and Hall generator probe are placed in an air-core solenoid which produces a field H opposing that of the magnet. Either the probe or the magnet is moved periodically along the axis of the solenoid. The probe output signal will also oscillate; as H is raised, the oscillations go through a minimum for $H = H_{ci}$. Higher-resolution measurements can be made by adding a second probe, placed under one end of the stationary magnet; it responds only to the vertical component of the magnet's field. The output signal of this probe varies as H is changed, becoming zero when $H = H_{ci}$. The vertical probe then measures the value of H. In practice, such coercimeters are accurate to within $\pm 1 \cdot 5\%$. A direct-reading permeameter can be built by the use of Hall generator or magnetoresistor probes, as shown in Figure 6.8. In order to measure B, a gap is required in the permeameter yoke. The gap has a high magnetic reluctance, which can be made negligible if the length of the alloy magnets tested is more than ~ 50 times and that of ceramic magnets is more than 20 times that of the gap length, and also by making the gap cross-sectional area at least one order of magnitude greater than the magnet surface area. A further reduction in the reluctance of the gap can be achieved by enclosing the Hall generators or magnetoresistor probe in soft ferrite cores. The potentiometer in Figure 6.8 is used to provide a ratio of the voltage produced by the B probe to the indicating meter according to the ratio of gap length to area, so that the meter can be calibrated directly in units of flux density. If it is required that the magnetization $I_M = B - H$ be measured as a function of H, then a second field probe placed close to the surface of the magnet can be used to

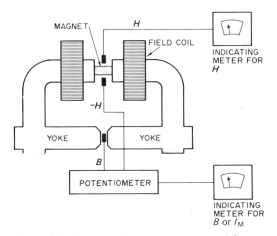

Figure 6.8. Direct reading permeameter used for measuring the significant magnetic parameters of magnetic materials; Hall probes are used to measure magnetomotive force H and magnetic induction B.

produce a negative signal proportional to H, which is then applied to the indicating meter.

A simple and sensitive susceptibility meter can be constructed by using a magnetic flux bridge circuit, as shown by Hilsum and Rose-Innes [106]. Figure 6.9 represents the equivalence between the flux bridge and that of an electrical bridge circuit used for potentiometric measurements. The magnetic reluctance of the permanent magnets is the analog of the internal resistance R_B of the batteries, and the variable resistances R_1 and R_2 are the analogs of the reluctances of the two air gaps. A Hall generator, or alternatively, a magnetoresistance bridge circuit performs the function of a detector of a flux unbalance. If a specimen with a magnetic permeability greater than unity is inserted in one of the air gaps, the circuit is unbalanced. The magnitude of the unbalance which can be detected depends on the sensitivity of the Hall generator or magnetoresistor elements. Assuming the limit to be ~1 mG and the field in the gap to be ~2 kG, then a change in reluctance of one part per million can readily be detected; this is a sensitivity sufficient for measuring the susceptibility of deionized water [106].

Miniature Hall probes can be used for mapping, on a microscale, the spatial magnetic flux distribution about ferromagnetic bodies [100]. A Hall probe mounted on motor-driven fixtures can be used to detect and plot, as a function of position, the static magnetic domain configuration and the residual flux distribution on magnetic tapes, bulk materials, and films. Film Hall probes of bismuth, 10 to 50 μm square (sensitive area) and 2 to 20 μm thick, were used [100–102] for field mapping of the flux pattern of tape-recording heads and drums. The Hall probe was mounted on a toolmaker's microscope stage. The lead screw of the stage was driven by a synchronous motor coupled to a multiturn potentiometer representing one arm of a bridge circuit. The signal proportional to the probe displacement, derived from the latter, was connected to the X axis input

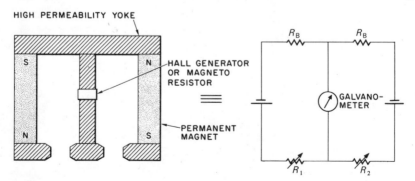

Figure 6.9. Magnetic susceptibility meter employing two permanent magnets, a high magnetic permeability yoke, and a Hall generator or magnetoresistance bridge; circuit is equivalent to a Wheatstone bridge (after Hilsum and Rose-Innes [106]).

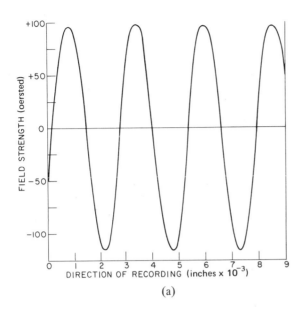

(a)

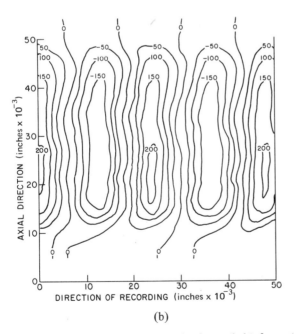

(b)

Figure 6.10. Magnetic field strength of recorded information on magnetic media measured by means of a subminiature (25 μm diameter) Hall generator: (a) magnetic field normal to surface of conventional iron oxide magnetic tape; (b) magnetic field distribution about recorded binary 'ones' plated on a cobalt–nickel memory drum; contour lines are in Oe.

of an *XY* recorder and the *Y* input to the Hall generator output. An isometric projection of the magnetic induction normal to the surface of a magnetized body can be prepared in this manner for fields greater than 5 mG. Typical results, illustrated in Figure 6.10, show the magnetic fields normal to the surface of a standard magnetic oxide tape, on which a series of 'ones' have been recorded with a density of 6×10^3 bits per inch, and the field distribution normal to a plated cobalt–nickel memory drum of a series of 'ones' recorded with a bit density of 88 bits per inch. Because the Hall probe must be moved in close proximity to the tape or other ferromagnetic object, whose residual flux may be slight, a number of problems arise which need to be taken into account in the course of such measurements. In mapping high-gradient fields, error voltages can be induced in the Hall probe owing to its motion in the field. This can be circumvented by driving the Hall generator with a.c. of a frequency much higher than the mechanical displacement rate of the Hall probe and also by using a narrow band system for processing the Hall output signal. One other source of error is the magnetic induction generated in the specimen to be measured by the magnetic field produced by the input current applied to the Hall probe. This problem is of particular significance in the flux mapping of low-coercivity materials. This source of error can be eliminated or reduced to negligible proportions by the use of a noninductive Hall generator configuration, as described by Kuhrt and Hartel [103] who evaluated these inductive effects in detail.

If the magnetic field to be measured is a periodic function of time, then a stroboscopic sampling method may be employed, in conjunction with a pulse-driven Hall generator, for mapping the field distribution. The wave form as well as the amplitude and direction of a time-varying magnetic field can be determined and the advantages inherent in (signal-to-noise gain) sampling procedures can also be realized. A sampling

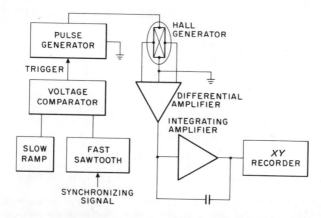

Figure 6.11. Stroboscopic sampling magnetometer for measuring periodic time-varying magnetic flux distributions in the frequency range between 10^2 Hz and 1 MHz.

magnetometer using an InSb film Hall generator vacuum-deposited on a glass substrate and mounted between ferrite flux concentrators was described by Wieder [104, 105]. It was used to determine the magnitude and direction of sinusoidal magnetic induction in the frequency range between 10^2 and 10^6 Hz with a sensitivity of 10^{-4} V G^{-1} by means of the apparatus shown schematically in Figure 6.11. The amplitude of the fast sawtooth signal, synchronized with the magnetic field to be measured, is compared against a slowly rising ramp voltage by a voltage comparator circuit. Its output, in turn, triggers a pulse generator, which applies a rectangular current pulse of ~9 mA and duration $\tau_1 = 0 \cdot 1$ μs at a rate, $\nu = 10^6$ pulses s^{-1} to the Hall generator. The current pulses thus sample stroboscopically the magnetic field and produce a Hall voltage v_h, whose peak value is the product of the peak pulse current and the instantaneous value of the magnetic field. After suitable amplification and integration of v_h, a low-frequency ($0 \cdot 1$ to 1 Hz) replica of the magnetic field is obtained, whose linearity is better than 2% (full scale) for B between 10^{-3} and 10^4 G.

6.4 Current transducers

Magnetic fields are associated with electric currents flowing in solids or with streams of charged particles in vacuum. Hall generators and magnetoresistors are capable of detecting and measuring such fields. They can act, therefore, as current transducers. The sensitivity of such current transducers can be increased considerably by mounting the Hall generator or magnetoresistance probe in the gap of a high-permeability yoke or ring surrounding the current to be measured [107, 108]. This is the basis for a clip-on ammeter capable of measuring the current in a wire or bus bar without breaking its circuit continuity. Currents down to $0 \cdot 1$ A can be measured in this manner without any amplification [107].

If the yoke is composed of two soft ferromagnetic C cores with identical gaps Δl between them, in which the Hall generators or magnetoresistor probes are placed, and I, the current to be measured, is enclosed between the C cores, then

$$\oint H ds = (H_1 + H_2)\Delta l + H_c l_c = I\mu_0 , \qquad (6.15)$$

where H_1 and H_2 are the respective fields in the gaps, H_c is the field within the yoke, l_c its corresponding path length, and μ_0 is the permeability of free space.

From Equation (6.15) the sum of the magnetic fields $H_1 + H_2$ is proportional to I provided that $H_c l_c / I \ll 1$. Two Hall generators with their output circuits connected in series, mounted in the gaps between the C cores, measure the respective fields H_1 and H_2 and provide a combined output proportional to I, in accordance with Equation (6.15).

Current transducers of one or more Hall generators, mounted in the air gaps of massive soft-iron yokes, can be used [109] to monitor and to measure large d.c. currents (5 to 400 kA). If Si–Fe is used as the material for the yoke, then current measurements to better than one part in a thousand can be made for $I \geqslant 15$ kA. Several considerations apply in the design and construction of high-current transducers: (1) the magnetic circuit should be free of nonlinear B, H phenomena and saturation effects; (2) the magnetic inductions in the multiple air gaps should be identical; (3) external ferromagnetic bodies placed near the yoke or current-carrying conductors should not perturb the field distribution in the respective gaps. The first two conditions can be met by the use of a material with a high saturation induction and careful control of the geometry of the yoke. The last condition is most easily met if the air gaps Δl are as narrow as possible, consistent with the other two conditions.

A sensitive clip-on current meter based on the flux-gate principle is shown in Figure 6.12. A Hall generator is mounted in the air gap of a ferrite or permalloy tape toroid, which is driven into saturation by a magnetomotive force derived from an alternating current source of frequency $\nu = 10$ kHz. Within the toroid, the permeability is a function of the m.m.f.; it is small except during the process of flux reversal from positive to negative saturation. For a sinusoidal magnetizing current, the m.m.f. opens and closes the (flux) 'permeability gate' twice per cycle. The large permeability of the toroid during flux reversal makes it behave as a flux concentrator of the field produced by the d.c. current I shown in Figure 6.12a. The reluctance of the air gap $\Re = K/f(2\nu)$, where K is a constant of proportionality and $f(2\nu)$ is a function which depends on the second harmonic of the driving frequency. The magnetic induction in the air gap is proportional to $If(2\nu)$. The magnetic field of the unknown current I modulates the amplitude of the second harmonic of ν and produces a 20 kHz output signal in the Hall generator. Figure 6.12b shows schematically the principal components of the current meter: the current transducer, the 20 kHz tuned amplifier, and the synchronous detector whose output is applied to the d.c. amplifier and the calibrated indicator. The negative feedback loop, shown in Figure 6.12b, provides a d.c. biasing flux to the current transducer. This improves the stability and the resolution of the instrument and allows the indicator to be nulled prior to effecting a measurement; the effective d.c. field acting on the current transducer is the difference between the field produced by the current I and that produced by the biasing current (Figure 6.12a).

A method of measurement of large currents (d.c.) of the order of 10^4A, by means of Hall generators, without employing a ferromagnetic yoke, has been suggested by Serkov [110]. It is based on the use of an integrating loop; identical Hall generators are spaced at a distance Δl from each other around a closed loop about the current to be measured.

Let the angle α_i be included between the magnetic field vector and the normal to one of the Hall plates denoted by the subscript i. The approximate relation

$$(H_1 \cos\alpha_1 + H_2 \cos\alpha_2 + \ldots H_m \cos\alpha_m)\Delta l = \sum_{i=1}^{m} H_i \cos\alpha_i \, \Delta l \approx \mu_0 I \qquad (6.16)$$

is presumed to be valid. The Hall voltage of a single Hall generator is taken to be $v_{hi} = (R_h/d)i_1 H_i \cos\alpha_i$, and for m Hall generators whose output circuits are connected in parallel the mean Hall voltage

$$\langle v_h \rangle = \sum_{i=1}^{m} v_{hi}/m \; .$$

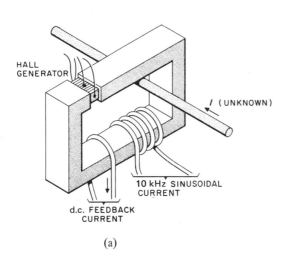

(a)

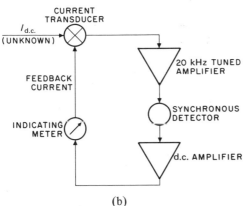

(b)

Figure 6.12. Current transducer based on flux-gate principle: (a) details of Hall sensor; (b) principal components of transducer.

Then, as a consequence of Equation (6.16),

$$I \approx \frac{\langle v_h \rangle (m \Delta l) d}{R_h i_1 \mu_0} \, . \qquad\qquad\qquad (6.17)$$

The current to be measured is thus a linear function of $\langle v_h \rangle$, provided that the parameters of the Hall generators are identical and i_1, the input current, is the same for all of them. The error of measurement evidently decreases as m increases and is smallest for an annular ring Hall generator ($m = \infty$). Serkov [110] suggests that at least eight, and not more than 20, discrete Hall generators are needed to maintain a tolerable error in measuring I without a ferromagnetic yoke.

Analog computer components

The applications of Hall generators and magnetoresistors as analog computer circuit components are based on the multiplying action inherent in galvano-magnetic phenomena. The following sections describe the basic structure and applications of Hall effect and magnetoresistance multipliers as well as the corollary uses, such as squaring, square root, and ratio computers, of importance for industrial process control. A satisfactory implementation of such analog computer functions depends not only on material parameters of Hall generators and magnetoresistors, discussed in earlier sections, but also on the configuration of the associated magnetic circuit. The latter should satisfy all, or most, of the following requirements: (1) the materials used should have a high saturation flux density; (2) they should have a high incremental permeability and a low reluctance; (3) hysteresis losses and eddy currents should be minimized; (4) the stacking factor of the solenoid, in which a magnetizing current provides the magnetomotive force, and the geometrical configuration of its magnetic core should be chosen so as to minimize flux leakage from the air gaps.

A material with a magnetic saturation induction B_s, a residual induction B_r, and a coercivity H_c, employed in a magnetic circuit with an air gap of length l_a, has a sheared hysteresis loop. The fractional hysteresis error $\eta_B \approx B_r/B_s$ for a ferromagnetic path length l_c is

$$\eta_B = \frac{H_c l_c}{B_s l_a + H_c l_c} . \tag{7.1}$$

Table 7.1 provides selected data for a number of materials, including η_B at d.c. and at 60 Hz, for a magnetic circuit with $l_c = 10$ cm and $l_a = 0.037$ cm.

Table 7.1. Some material parameters of soft and hard ferromagnetic materials.

Material	B_s (kG)	d.c. coercivity H_c (Oe)	d.c. hysteresis error η_{dc}	60 Hz hysteresis error η_{60}
Deltamax	14	0·10	0·195	0·42
Orthonol	14	0·10	0·195	0·42
Supermendur	22	0·10	0·120	1·20
μ-metal	4·5	0·02	0·120	
Armco M-6X	14	0·10	0·212	
Permalloy	6·0	0·04	0·180	0·34
Supermalloy	6·5	0·005	0·022	0·147
Hy-μ 80	6·5	0·02	0·09	0·18
Orthosil	13	0·27	0·56	
Permendur	20	2·3	3·04	

If the solenoid providing the magnetomotive force to the magnetic circuit is fed from a voltage source (internal impedance = 0), then the magnetizing current

$$i_\text{m} = \frac{V_i}{R_\text{m} + j\omega L} \tag{7.2}$$

where R_m is the d.c. winding resistance and L the inductance of the solenoid having N turns and a cross-sectional area A. For $l_\text{a}\mu/l_\text{c} \gg 1$ the magnetic induction in the air gap $B \approx 1 \cdot 25 N i_\text{m} l_\text{a}$ and the inductance

$$L \approx \frac{1 \cdot 25 N^2 A}{l_\text{a}} . \tag{7.3}$$

Assuming an equivalent 3 decibel drop in i for $f = f_\text{max}$ due to the dependence of the inductive reactance on frequency,

$$f_\text{max} = \frac{R_\text{m}}{2\pi L} . \tag{7.4}$$

The bandwidth of the magnetic circuit is limited by L, since f_max increases as L decreases. If, on the other hand, the m.m.f. is provided by a current source (internal impedance = ∞), then i_m is frequency-independent. In practice, a constant current source having a finite internal impedance Z_i will introduce a bandwidth limitation; however, if $Z_\text{i} \gg R_\text{m}$, then $f_\text{max} = Z_\text{i}/2\pi L$, and thus the bandwidth will be larger than that of a circuit driven from a voltage source.

Ferromagnetic alloys, such as listed in Table 7.1, may be formed into ribbons and laminated. Such magnetic cores may be used in magnetic circuits operating at frequencies up to $0 \cdot 2$ MHz. However, hysteresis

Table 7.2. Figures of merit of various magnetic materials; $Q = \omega L/R$, where L is the inductance and R the resistance of the solenoid supplying magnetomotive force (after Cosgriff, R. L., 1966, *Solid-State Electron.*, **9**, 360).

Material	Frequency Hz	Initial permeability μ	μQ	Saturation induction kG
MnZn ferrite	10^6	$1 \cdot 5 \times 10^3$	$1 \cdot 5 \times 10^4$	
	10^5	$1 \cdot 4 \times 10^3$	2×10^5	
NiZn ferrite	10^6	90	$1 \cdot 5 \times 10^4$	
	10^5	90	$1 \cdot 5 \times 10^4$	
Ferramic Q-1	10^6	400	5×10^4	$3 \cdot 30$
Ferramic H	10^6	850	3×10^4	$3 \cdot 40$
Mo permalloy	10^6	14	10^3	
(Powder)	10^5	14	10^4	
(Powder)	$1 \cdot 8 \times 10^3$	125	$4 \cdot 7 \times 10^4$	

losses are large at the higher frequencies. Ferrite cores are useful in the frequency range between 50 kHz and 10 MHz; however, magnetization phenomena above 1 MHz are complex and the saturation induction of high-frequency ferrite is low[1]. Alternatively, pressed powder cores, such as those listed in Table 7.2, can be used to achieve a linear B versus m.m.f. response and a high Q between $\sim 0 \cdot 2$ kHz and 10 MHz.

7.1 Hall effect multipliers

The output voltage v_h of a properly loaded Hall generator is the product of two input variables: the input current i_1 and the magnetizing current i_m flowing in an air core or magnetically-loaded solenoid which produces the transverse magnetic induction B. The output of the Hall generator is a relatively small voltage, while the input variables i_1 and i_m are relatively large currents. For some multiplier applications [116] this may be satisfactory. For others, such as analog computer functions, it is more advantageous to have the input and output signals in the form of voltages (of the same order of magnitude); a power gain for such a multiplier is also desirable in order that several units might be used in cascade, if necessary. This requires the use of buffer amplifiers in conjunction with the Hall generator. Other considerations include the bandwidth needed for processing a multiplication operation within a given time interval, dynamic linear range of the multiplier and its short- and long-term stability, resolution, and accuracy involving not only the Hall generator and its magnetic circuit, but other components and circuits associated with the multiplier.

A number of initial choices are available to the designer of Hall multipliers. These include the type of material and the geometrical configuration used for the construction of Hall plates and the method of linearization of the i_m versus B response of the magnetic circuit. Löfgren [111, 112], in his two classical papers, has analyzed these considerations in detail. He concluded that silicon Hall plates are desirable for multiplier functions because of their thermal stability, high linearity, and high input and output impedances, which are compatible with vacuum tube circuits. The availability of $InAs_{0.8}P_{0.2}$ and of thin-film III–V compound Hall generators suggests, however, that, for multipliers operated in conjunction with transistor amplifiers, these materials are preferred for present day or contemplated device applications. Löfgren [112] also described a feedback method for increasing the linearity of the magnetic circuit. The procedure is shown schematically in Figure 7.1. An input voltage v_a produces a current I_0 in a control Hall generator placed in the same air gap as the Hall generator performing as a multiplier. The output signal of the control Hall generator drives a differential power amplifier

[1] For a comprehensive treatment of ferrite or ferromagnetic alloy-cored solenoids and transformers, the reader is referred to Velsby, V. G., 1960, *The Theory and Design of Inductance Coils* (John Wiley, New York).

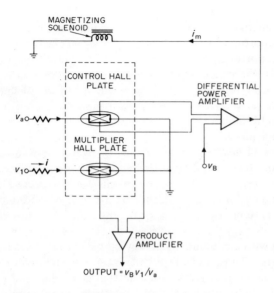

Figure 7.1. Linearization of Hall multiplier by means of second Hall generator in feedback loop (after Löfgren [112]).

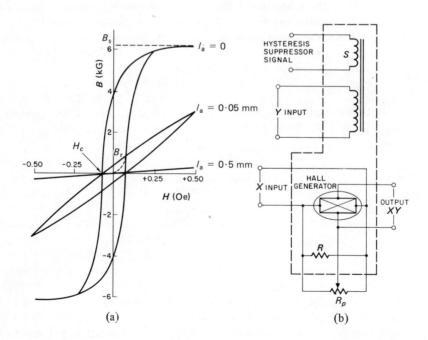

Figure 7.2. B versus H hysteresis of ferromagnetic circuit: (a) dependence of saturation induction and coercive force on air-gap length; (b) suppression of hysteresis error by superposition of a.c. flux component on steady B.

which provides the magnetizing current i_m. The feedback loop sets the magnetic induction proportional to v_B. The output signal from the product amplifier is proportional to $v_1 v_B / v_a$.

For d.c. input signals, the magnetic circuit nonlinearity is due to hysteresis errors. It can be reduced by increasing the length of the gap, as shown in Figure 7.2a, at the expense of a higher m.m.f. required to achieve the same magnetic induction. A nonlinearity of less than 1% is desirable. This can be achieved by operating the multiplier in a single quadrant (all positive or all negative input signals) or by superposing an a.c. component [113] on the d.c. flux of sufficient magnitude to overcome the coercive force of material. The frequency of this error corrective flux is to be at least one order of magnitude higher than the highest frequency at which the multiplier is to be used. A circuit for this purpose is illustrated in Figure 7.2b.

Multipliers operating with a.c. input signals have some definite advantages over d.c. Hall multipliers. These include the absence of hysteresis errors, suppression of misalignment error voltages in the Hall generator, and of null-point drift associated with d.c. amplifiers. At the higher frequencies errors arise due to phase shift between the voltage and current in the magnetic circuit. The phase shift can be minimized by keeping the $Q = \omega L / R$ of the solenoid as small as possible or by the use of feedback, as shown by Greiner [114] and illustrated schematically in Figure 7.3. If the feedback current is zero, then $i_m = v_0 / (R + j\omega L)$ and the feedback voltage $v_F = i_m R$ is

$$v_F = \frac{v_0 R}{R + j\omega L}.$$ (7.5)

The amplifier is presumed to have a voltage gain G, and its output voltage is consequently $v_0 = G(v_i - v_F)$. In the presence of feedback, the current i_m is then

$$i_m = \frac{v_i}{R(1 + 1/G) + j\omega L/G} \approx \frac{v_i}{R + j\omega L/G}.$$ (7.6)

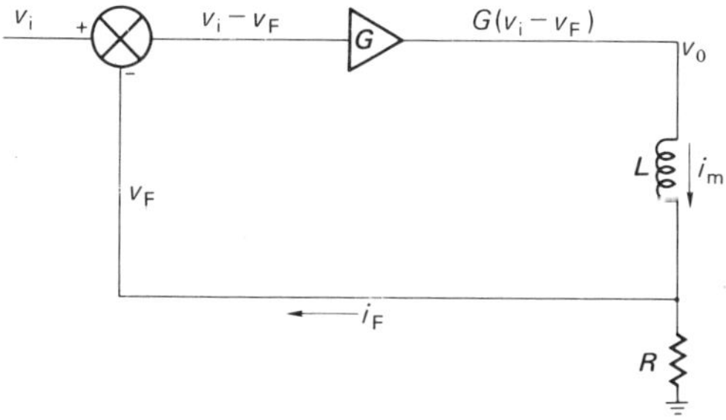

Figure 7.3. Equivalent circuit of a.c. feedback loop of Hall multiplier used to eliminate phase shift between magnetic induction and Hall generator input current (after Greiner [114]).

Thus, for $G \gg 1$, feedback reduces the magnitude of the inductive reactance by the value of the open-loop gain (see also Chapter 7) and decreases the phase shift. The highest frequency ν_1 at which the voltage and current in the solenoid are still in phase may be expressed as

$$\nu_1 = \frac{QRG}{2\pi L} .$$ (7.7)

For many applications, it is desirable to refer the output voltage of a multiplier to ground. However, the output has common-mode signals impressed upon it which may be many times greater than the desired product signal. Common-mode signal rejection can be enhanced by the use of difference amplifiers (with common-mode rejection ratios of the order of 10^4 to 1). It may also be reduced by applying a small d.c. current to the solenoid in addition to the a.c. input signal to be multiplied. If the input to the solenoid is of the form $V_{dc} + V_1 \cos \omega_1 t$ and that applied to the Hall generator is $V_2 \cos \omega_2 t$, then the output of their product, from the difference amplifier, is [114]

$$V_{out} = K_1 (V_{dc} + V_1 \cos \omega_1 t) V_2 \cos \omega_2 t + K_2 V_2 \cos \omega_2 t ,$$ (7.8)

where $K_2 V_2 \cos \omega_2 t$ is the common-mode signal in the difference amplifier (including any null-point error voltage present). Expanding Equation (7.8), we have

$$V_{out} = K_1 V_{dc} V_2 \cos \omega_2 t + K_1 V_1 V_2 \cos \omega_1 t \cos \omega_2 t + K_2 V_2 \cos \omega_2 t .$$ (7.9)

If V_{dc} is so chosen that $-K_1 V_{dc} = K_2$, then, from Equation (7.9), only the desired product term of the two input signals

$$V_{out} = K_1 V_1 V_2 \cos \omega_1 t \cos \omega_2 t$$ (7.10)

will appear in the output of the multiplier.

Hall multipliers for radio frequencies (beyond ~ 1 MHz) pose additional problems for the designer. These include inductive coupling between the input and output circuits of the Hall generator and a difficulty in canceling the misalignment voltage by resistive-bridge techniques. Cohen [115] has shown the misalignment voltage can be corrected by a superposed d.c. flux and that a wide-band transformer can be used to provide isolation between the input and output circuits. Inductive coupling can be reduced to 50 dB below the maximum Hall signal, and useful multiplier operation can be achieved between $\sim 0 \cdot 1$ MHz and ~ 10 MHz.

Saraga and Galpin [117] have shown that Hall generators may also be used as vector multipliers, $\bar{E}_h = R_h (\bar{B} \times \bar{J})$. For example: two coplanar input vectors $\bar{B}$ and $\bar{J}$, each of constant length, are constrained to rotate in the (x, y) plane. The first has an angular velocity ω_1 and the second has an angular velocity $\pm \omega_2$. Their vector product is another vector in the z direction

$$E_h = KBJ \sin(\omega_1 \mp \omega_2) t ,$$ (7.11)

where K is a constant of proportionality[2]. The negative sign applies when both vectors are rotating in the same sense, and the positive sign pertains to counterrotating vectors. For a time vector product, the output signal is *either* the sum *or* the difference of the input frequencies, in contrast with scalar multiplication which presents the sum of *both*. Experimental verification of Equation (7.11) was made on a cruciform InSb Hall plate mounted in a four-pole magnetic circuit; a conversion efficiency of -50 dB was obtained for $B = 45$ G and -23 dB for $13 = 1$ kG at frequencies up to 15 MHz.

Wide-band Hall multipliers, based on the modulation of a radio-frequency carrier, can be built in accordance with the description of Claudin and Fric [118]. Let $v_1(t)$ and $v_2(t)$ be input signals with frequency spectra from 0 to $\omega_1/2\pi$ and 0 to $\omega_2/2\pi$ respectively. Hall generators are used to multiply these input signals with the same carrier $V\cos\omega t$ so chosen that $\omega \gg \omega_1$ or ω_2. The input signals $v_1(t)$ and $v_2(t)$ are applied as currents to the respective Hall generators, and the carrier provides the magnetic inductions for each of them. The output signal of the first Hall generator, after suitable amplification, drives a magnetizing solenoid with the signal $K_1 v_1(t)\cos\omega t$, and the output signal derived from the second Hall generator, $K_2 v_2(t)\cos\omega t$, drives the input current of a third Hall generator whose transverse induction is provided by the magnetizing solenoid. The output of the third Hall generator is of the form $K_1 K_2 v_1(t)v_2(t) V^2 \cos^2 \omega t$. A low-pass filter eliminates the components $v_1(t)v_2(t)\cos 2\omega t$, $[2\omega \gg (\omega_1 + \omega_2)]$, and yields the product $v_1(t)v_2(t)$. Many of the perturbations and error voltages, which arise in Hall multiplication, are eliminated because the voltages produced by the spectral range from $(\omega + \omega_1)/2\pi$ to $(\omega - \omega_1)/2\pi$ are quite different from those produced by the product $v_1(t)v_2(t),,$ which are contained in the spectral range between 0 and $(\omega_1 + \omega_2)/2\pi$. Using a.c. input signals from $0\cdot 5$ kHz to $0\cdot 1$ MHz, Claudin and Fric [118] managed to obtain a 3% (full-scale) accuracy for a dynamic range (limited by amplifier saturation) between 0 and 45 mV. The technique also illustrates the potential application of Hall multipliers as wide-band modulators.

A typical four-quadrant Hall multiplier built by Kovatch and Meserve [119] using a 'silectron' iron core and an indium arsenide Hall generator had the following properties: the Hall generator circuit had a flat response from 0 to 10 kHz with a bandwidth of 25 kHz and a phase shift of $18°$ at 10 kHz. The magnetic circuit was flat to only $0\cdot 4$ kHz; Its bandwidth was limited to $1\cdot 3$ kHz and it had a phase shift of $15°$ at $0\cdot 4$ kHz. The static error[3] of the Hall circuit for ±50 V input was

---

[2] The same multiplication can be performed by means of two conventional Hall effect multipliers instead of a single vector multiplier [117].

[3] A detailed discussion of the static errors of Hall multipliers was given by Jaworski, J., Nalecz, M., Zawicki, I., 1966, *Solid-State Electron.*, **9**, 515, and by Billings and Lloyd [134].

±0·8% full scale. The error of the magnetic circuit, over the same range, was ±2·8%.

7.2 Magnetoresistance multipliers
One of the basic building-blocks of magnetoresistance multipliers is the magnetoresistance bridge circuit shown schematically in Figure 7.4a. The mesh equations of this circuit are

$$V = i_1 R_1 + i_3 R_L$$

$$-V = i_3 R_L - i_2 R_2$$

$$i_1 = i_2 + i_3 ,$$ (7.12)

where the potentials V are considered to be voltage sources $R(B)_{1,2} = R_{1,2}$ and the output voltage $v_o = i_3 R_L$ is

$$v_o = \frac{V(R_2 - R_1)}{R_1 + R_2 + R_1 R_2 / R_L} ,$$ (7.13)

and, if $R_L \gg R_1 R_2$, then v_o is essentially the open-circuit bridge output signal

$$\frac{v_o}{V} \approx \frac{R_2 - R_1}{R_2 + R_1} .$$ (7.14)

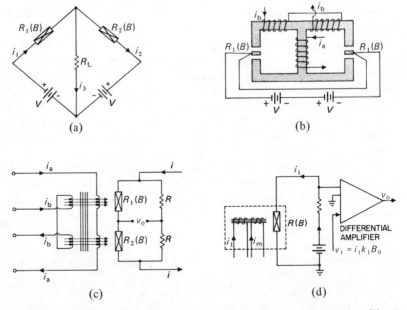

Figure 7.4. Magnetoresistor multiplier circuits: (a) basic building blocks; (b) magneto-resistor bridge circuit and associated magnetic circuit; (c) multiplication of three input variables; (d) half-bridge circuit operated in linear $R(B)$ versus B range.

The magnetic circuit shown in Figure 7.4b consists of a ferromagnetic E core. The magnetoresistors R_1 and R_2 are placed in the air gaps, and counterwound solenoids (on the outer legs of the transformer) produce magnetic fluxes of equal magnitude, but opposed in direction. The solenoid on the center leg of the transformer is traversed by the magnetizing current i_a, which generates identical magnetic inductions B_a in the two air gaps. Suppose that a current i_b flows through the outer solenoids generating the magnetic inductions $+B_b$ and $-B_b$ in the air gaps, where they add to B_a, producing respectively $B_1 = B_a + B_b$ and $B_2 = B_a - B_b$. The magneto-resistors R_1 and R_2 are presumed to have a quadratic dependence on B and their zero-field values $R_1(0) = R_2(0) = R_0$. In consequence,

$$R_1 = R_0 [1 + k(B_a + B_b)^2]$$
$$R_2 = R_0 [1 + k(B_a - B_b)^2] \, . \qquad (7.15)$$

The coefficient k is a function of the electron mobility, magnetoresistor geometry, microscopic distribution of conductive inclusions within it, and of its effective temperature. Introducing Equation (7.15) into Equation (7.14), we have

$$\frac{v_o}{V} = \frac{2kB_aB_b}{1 + k(B_a^2 + B_b^2)} \, . \qquad (7.16)$$

Provided that the magnetic inductions are linear functions of the magnetizing current and that $k(B_a^2 + B_b^2) \ll 1$, Equation (7.16) can be expressed as

$$v_o = Ci_ai_b V \, , \qquad (7.17)$$

where the coefficient of proportionality C includes the terms which represent the proportionality between the m.m.f.'s and B_a and B_b, respectively, as well as the factor $2k$. Equation (7.17) is the basis of a simple magnetoresistance multiplier; with V and C held constant, the output voltage of the magnetoresistor bridge circuit is proportional to the product of the independent variables i_a and i_b.

The multiplication of three variables can be accomplished [120, 121] by means of the circuit shown in Figure 7.4c, where i is the additional variable and R is a linear resistance. Provided that $R \gg R(B)_{1,2}$ the unloaded bridge output voltage is

$$v_u = C_1 i_a i_b i \, . \qquad (7.18)$$

The methods and techniques used for linearization of the magnetic circuit discussed at the beginning of Chapter 7 and in Section 7.1 are also applicable to magnetoresistance multipliers. A simple and effective multiplier may be built in accordance with Figure 7.4d. In high magnetic fields, thin-film (InSb + In) magnetoresistors have a linear dependence on the magnetic induction, as shown in Figure 5.6. Suppose that the current i_B provides a biasing magnetic induction $B_0 \approx 6\,\text{kG}$ acting on the magnetoresistor $R(B)$, which is much smaller than the linear resistor R. The effective resistance $R(B) = k_1(B_0 \pm B)$, where k_1 is a constant of proportionality. The output voltage v_0 in the circuit shown in Figure 7.4d is

$$v_0 = C_2 i_m i_1 \tag{7.19}$$

where C_1 is a coefficient proportional to k_1 and to the m.m.f.

A magnetoresistance multiplier [121, 122] with a wide dynamic range capable of performing the multiplication of two input variables (0 to 10 V) with an accuracy to better than $0 \cdot 5\%$ is shown in Figure 7.5. It consists of two independent potentiometers, each made up of a magnetoresistor $R(B)_{1,2}$ and a linear resistor R. The reference potentiometer has two identical input potentials $\pm V_r$ and an output x applied to one of the input terminals of a differential amplifier with a voltage gain K_1. The arbitrary input voltage X is applied to its other input terminal. The amplifier output signal e is fed to a power amplifier K_2. This furnishes the solenoid of the electromagnet. The latter provides the magnetic induction B, which acts identically upon both magnetoresistors $R_1(B)$ and $R_2(B)$. The follow-up potentiometer is connected to the independent input potential Y, and its output voltage $v = Yr(B)$. The quantity $r(B)$ is dimensionless and is derived in the same way as Equation (7.14): $r(B) = (R_2 - R)/(R_2 + R)$. The differential amplifier output signal is

$$e = K_1(X - x), \tag{7.20}$$

and that of the power amplifier is a magnetic induction $B(i) \propto K_2 e$, produced in the air gap of the electromagnet by the current i; therefore

$$B(i) \propto K_1 K_2(X - x). \tag{7.21}$$

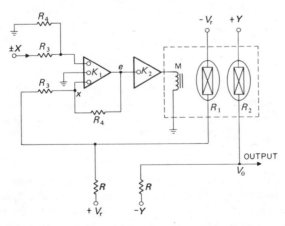

Figure 7.5. Feedback multiplier with two magnetoresistors R_1 and R_2 in the same air gap of a magnetic circuit; X and Y are arbitrary input variables and V_r is a reference potential; K_1 and K_2 are, respectively, voltage and power amplifiers.

The reference potentiometer output signal is $x = V_r r(B)$, and the feedback loop around the amplifier constrains equality of the two inputs of the differential amplifier; thus, in the steady-state condition, $x = X$ and the multiplier output is

$$v_o = \frac{XY}{V_r} . \tag{7.22}$$

In order to obtain Equation (7.22), it has been assumed, implicitly, that the two magnetoresistors R_1 and R_2 exhibit perfect 'tracking'. This requires that their initial resistances as well as their magnetoresistance coefficients be identical. Furthermore, the linear resistors R must be matched to eliminate intrinsic multiplication errors. The reference potential V_r in Equation (7.22) is obviously a scaling factor. For convenience, if X and Y are of the same order of magnitude, V_r may be chosen so that v_o is in the same units as X and Y or in some convenient decimal scale.

A similar system using two complete magnetoresistance bridge circuits was described by Gitlin [123, 124] and is shown schematically in Figure 7.6. The magnetic circuit has a permanent magnet with a magnetic

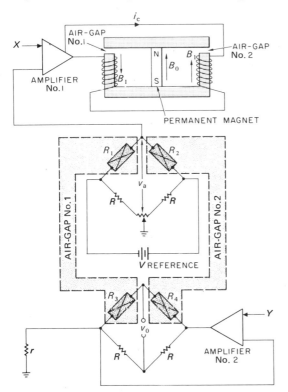

Figure 7.6. Magnetoresistor multiplier employing two magnetoresistor bridge circuits and feedback for extending frequency response and dynamic range of multiplier.

induction B_0 in its center leg. The X input drives a power amplifier in a negative feedback loop, which includes the counterwound magnetizing solenoids on the outer legs of the transformer. The magnetic induction in the air gaps is either the sum (air gap No.1) or the difference (air gap No.2) of B_0 and that of B_1, the flux produced in consequence of the input signal X. The magnetoresistors R_1 and R_3 are mounted in air gap No.1 and R_2 and R_4 in air gap No.2. The bridge circuits are adjusted for a null and $R_1 + R_2 = R_3 + R_4$. The magnetoresistors are presumed to have a quadratic dependence on B:

$$R_1 = R_3 = R_0[1 + k(B_0 + B_1)^2]$$
$$R_2 = R_4 = R_0[1 + k(B_0 - B_1)^2].$$

(7.23)

Provided that $k(B_0^2 + B_1^2) \ll 1$, the output voltage of the reference bridge circuit $v_a = V_{ref}kB_0B_1$, and, if $kB_0 = C_3$, a constant of proportionality, then

$$v_a = C_3 V_{ref} B_1.$$

(7.24)

The magnetizing current of the solenoid is determined by the input potential difference $X - v_a$, the gain G_1 of amplifier No.1, and the impedance of the solenoid is $Z = R_c + j\omega L_c$; R_c is its resistance and L_c its inductance. The magnetizing current i_c is

$$i_c = G_1 \frac{X - C_3 V_{ref} B_1}{R_c + j\omega L_c}.$$

(7.25)

Let B_1 be proportional to i_c, $B_1 = C_4 i_c$; Equation (7.25) can then be written in the form

$$i_c = \frac{X}{C_3 C_4 V_{ref}}$$

(7.26)

provided that G_1 is large and that

$$\frac{G_1 C_3 C_4 V_{ref}}{R_c + j\omega L_c} \gg 1.$$

(7.27)

The output signal v_0 of the second magnetoresistance bridge circuit is

$$v_0 = Yi_c C_3 C_4 G_2 \left(1 - \frac{R}{r + R}\right)$$

(7.28)

where G_2 is the gain of amplifier No.2. Combining Equations (7.27) and (7.28), we have

$$v_0 = XY\left[\frac{G_2 r}{V_{ref}(r + R)}\right].$$

(7.29)

The advantage of magnetoresistors for multiplier applications is that many of the problems associated with Hall generators, such as the misalignment voltage, null-point fluctuations, and inductive coupling between input and output circuits, are absent owing to the fact that magnetoresistors are two-port rather than four-port devices. However, the inherent limitations in performance of either Hall or magnetoresistance multipliers are determined primarily by the magnetic circuits. Feedback linearizes and improves the frequency response of both types of multipliers at the expense of the inclusion of an active circuit to the passive multiplier systems.

7.3 Corollary analog computer functions

A large number of analog computer operations, the corollaries of multiplication, may be implemented by means of Hall generators and magnetoresistors. A simple circuit useful for generating the reciprocal of an arbitrary function [116], represented by the current i_m, is shown in Figure 7.7a. It consists of a Hall generator connected in the feedback loop of an amplifier, whose output provides the input current i_1 to the Hall generator. In the steady state the output voltage of the Hall

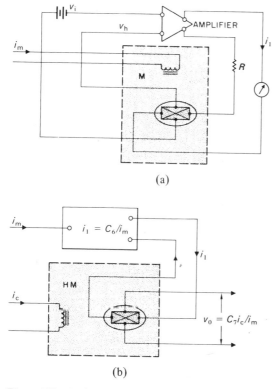

(a)

(b)

Figure 7.7. Analog computer applications of Hall generators: (a) current i_1 is a reciprocal function of the arbitrary input current i_m; (b) combination of reciprocal function generator and Hall multiplier HM used as ratio computer.

generator v_h is constrained to equality with the input voltage v_i. If the magnetic induction B, acting on the Hall generator, is proportional to i_m, then

$$v_h = v_i = C_5 i_m i_1 , \tag{7.30}$$

where C_5 is a constant proportional to the Hall coefficient of the Hall generator as well as to B; consequently,

$$i_1 = \frac{v_i}{C_5 i_m} = \frac{C_6}{i_m} . \tag{7.31}$$

Thus, with v_i fixed, the Hall generator input current is a reciprocal function of the magnetizing current i_m.

A ratio computer [116] can be assembled from a reciprocal function generator such as shown in Figure 7.7a, and a Hall multiplier whose input current is derived from the reciprocal function generator as shown in Figure 7.7b. For this purpose, the Hall generator of Figure 7.7a is simply connected in series with the Hall generator input current i_1, which is an integral part of the reciprocal function generator. Provided that i_c is proportional to the magnetic induction of the Hall multiplier, then its output voltage

$$v_o = C_7 \frac{i_c}{i_m} , \tag{7.32}$$

where C_7 is proportional to C_6 and to the Hall coefficient of the second Hall generator.

A ratio computer employing a single Hall generator [125, 126] in a feedback circuit is shown in Figure 7.8. The dash-enclosed rectangle X contains the Hall multiplier. Its output signal is applied to the input terminal a of the differential amplifier, whose other terminal b is connected to an arbitrary input signal v_i. The amplified difference signal is applied to a power amplifier which modulates the light intensity of the lamp l. The effective value of resistance of the photoresistor R is a function of the light intensity incident upon it. The dash-enclosed rectangle Y constitutes an electro-optic transducer, whose purpose is that of providing a feedback loop around the differential amplifier and to maintain a high degree of isolation between the input and output circuits of the Hall multiplier.

Suppose a current i_c is applied to the magnetizing solenoid and an input signal v_i is applied to the differential amplifier. The output signal drives the base of the 2N652 transistor into conduction, causing a current to flow through lamp l. The light output of the latter brings about a decrease in R, decreasing the bias of the 2N174 power transistor. A current i_h flows into the Hall generator, producing an output voltage v_h. The process continues, constrained by the feedback loop until $v_h = v_i$. Provided the misalignment voltage of the Hall generator is negligible and

the differential amplifier is balanced, the Hall current is proportional to
the ratio of v_i to i_c:

$$i_b = C_8 \frac{v_i}{i_c} . \tag{7.33}$$

Equation (7.33) is that of an equilateral hyperbola with asymptotes at
$i_c = 0$ and $i_b = 0$. In practice, a misalignment voltage in the Hall
generator, a residual magnetization in the core, or a finite unbalance in
the differential amplifier may cause an output signal to appear for $i_c = 0$.
This shifts the asymptote of i_c to the left or right of the coordinate axis,
and therefore to values of i_h which are finite for $i_c = 0$, thus reducing
the accuracy of the ratio computer. For the circuit shown [125] in
Figure 7.8, with $v_i = 50$ mV, the reciprocal Hall current i_b is proportional
to i_c to within 2% for 5 mA $\leqslant i_c \leqslant$ 35 mA.

Analog division of two a.c. input signals by means of a system employing
a Hall generator whose d.c. drive current represents their ratio has been
described by Hutcheon [127] and Hutcheon and Harrison [128]. It is
shown schematically in Figure 7.9. The Hall generator is connected in
the negative feedback loop around an a.c. amplifier and a demodulator.
The solenoid is energized by the a.c. reference current i_c, and the d.c.
output current i_{dc} from the demodulator is applied to the Hall generator.
The a.c. output voltage v_h proportional to the product $i_c i_{dc}$ is feedback
to the a.c. input amplifier. In the quiescent state, the a.c. input signal
v_i is constrained by the feedback loop so that $i_{dc} \propto v_i/i_c$. Multiplication

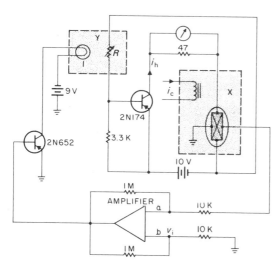

Figure 7.8. Analog division by means of single Hall generator with electro-optic
feedback coupling between input and output circuits; Hall current i_h is proportional
to ratio of v_i to i_c.

of an a.c. signal by a d.c. signal by means of Hall generators is of advantage
because electrode misalignment and magnetic hysteresis errors are reduced
to a large extent. The reference current i_c and the input voltage v_i must,
however, be of the same phase and frequency. If the amplifier has a suitably
high gain and the demodulator is correctly phased, then the accuracy of
the system depends almost entirely on that of the Hall generator itself.
In the steady state, demodulation takes place at low signal levels, typically
$1 \cdot 5 \, \mu A$, 5 mV. The demodulator is designed, however, to handle much
larger signals without saturation, typically $1 \cdot 5$ mA, 5 V; the system
completely rejects quadrature signals of any magnitude up to $\sim 100\%$
full-scale input. Another advantage of this analog divider is its capability
of responding without saturation to step changes of the input signal up to
100% full scale, i.e. it has the same response as a single-stage RC filter.

A transistorized analog a.c. ratio computer based on a similar principle
was described by Miteva and Vichev [129]. They used a Hall generator
made from an InSb film 6×3 mm vacuum-deposited in a mica substrate
held in the gap of a toroidal permalloy core, wherein it was fixed by
epoxy resin. At a frequency of 50 Hz, the dynamic range of the input
current i_c was $45:1$ and that of v_i, limited by the operational range of
the amplifiers, was found to be $\sim 6:1$.

A variety of arithmetic operations, including division [123, 124], may
be performed by means of magnetoresistance multipliers connected in
appropriate feedback loops. Sun [120, 121] has shown that, if the output
signals derived from two three-dimensional magnetoresistance multipliers
A and B

$$v_a = C_a i_1 i_2 i_3$$
$$v_b = C_b i_4 i_5 i_6 \tag{7.34}$$

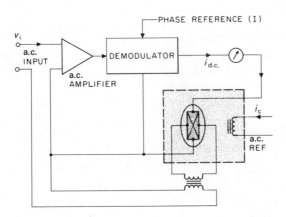

Figure 7.9. Analog division of two a.c. input signals v_i and i_c; the d.c. output i_{dc} is
proportional to their ratio.

are connected to the respective input terminals of a differential amplifier whose output current i_6 is applied to multiplier B in a feedback loop, then i_6 will reach a steady-state condition when $v_a = v_b$, and this results in

$$i_6 = \frac{C_a}{C_b} \frac{i_1 i_2 i_3}{i_4 i_5} . \tag{7.35}$$

Depending on the type and number of currents in Equation (7.35) held constant and those selected as independent variables, division, squaring, and square root operations (tabulated by Sun) may be performed by means of magnetoresistors.

Many problems in physics or engineering require the solution of the square root of the sum of the square of three independent variables. Wieder [130] has shown that such analog computer functions may be implemented by means of three Hall-effect squaring multipliers whose output signals are, in turn, applied to a linear adder. The output of the adder drives a d.c. square-root computer made up of a squaring multiplier and a feedback loop, such as shown in Figure 7.10. Miteva and Vichev [131] have built an a.c. square-root computer along the same principles using an InSb Hall probe in the air gap of a toroidal permalloy core and a circuit, previously described in connection with the ratio computer [129]. At a frequency of 50 Hz they obtained the square root of input voltages in the range $0 \cdot 2 \text{ mV} \leqslant v_i \leqslant 50 \text{ mV}$, with an accuracy better than 4%. A detailed analysis of square-root computers, using Hall multipliers, was given by Ohno and Ohta [132]. They used a nonlinear amplifier in the feedback loop and differential compensation circuit to obtain an accuracy of $\pm 0 \cdot 2\%$. They emphasized, in particular, the necessity for high closed-loop amplifier gain in order to reduce computer errors.

Multiple Hall plates connected in cascade lend themselves to the generation of complex polynomial functions [133]. If a Hall plate is driven from a constant current source in the air gap of a magnetic circuit whose magnetic induction is proportional to a variable x, then its output voltage may be represented as $K_1 x$, with K a constant. If a second Hall generator, in the same air gap, has its input leads connected to the output of the first, then, ignoring magnetoresistance and feedback errors [134], the output of the second Hall generator is $K_2 x^2$. Successive cascading of Hall generators will produce outputs $K_3 x^3, K_4 x^4, ..., K_n x^n$. If the output signals of each of the Hall plates are combined in a linear adder so that α_r times the open-circuit Hall voltage appears in its output,

$$V = \sum_{r=1}^{n} \alpha_r K_r x^r , \tag{7.36}$$

where $\alpha_r K_r$ is the modified polynomial coefficient. Billings [133] has shown that functions which are polynomials of more than one variable can be synthesized by means of an additional magnetic circuit. Magneto-resistors may also be used for generating polynomial functions of the form $y = Ax^3 + Bx^2 + Cx + D$, as shown by Kataoka and Yamada [135]. If a magnetizing solenoid in whose air gap a magnetoresistor is mounted is connected in series with that magnetoresistor, then, provided that $B = Kx$ and the magnetoresistor is driven in its square law, $R(B)$ versus B characteristic, the potential drop across $R(B)$ is a cubic function of x. A polynomial in $y(x)$, such as given above, can be generated by connecting a Hall generator and magnetoresistor whose input currents are driven in series and placed in the same air gap. Alternatively, the loading resistance across the Hall generator and other auxiliary linear resistors in a bridge circuit can be tailored in such a manner as to choose deliberately the magnitude of the cubic, quadratic, and linear coefficients of x.

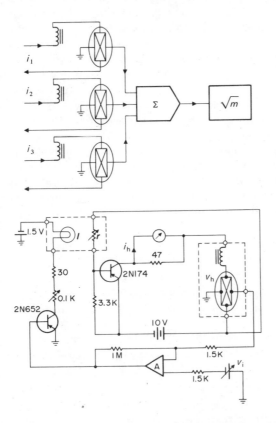

Figure 7.10. Computer for extracting the square root of the sum of the squares of three arbitrary input currents i_1, i_2, and i_3; Σ is a linear adder and $\sqrt{m}$ is a square-root computer shown in the lower diagram. It is a squaring multiplier with electro-optic feedback between its input and output circuits; i_h is proportional to $v_i^{1/2}$.

8

Wattmeters and power transducers

The power dissipated in a load impedance driven by d.c. or by an a.c. single-phase or polyphase distribution system and the reactive and virtual power present in transmission lines can be measured by means of wattmeters and power transducers employing Hall generators and magnetoresistors. A d.c. power transducer is simply a Hall generator in a magnetic circuit, whose magnetic induction is proportional to the current and whose input current i_1 is proportional to the voltage of the circuit element whose dissipation is to be determined   For a single-phase a.c. wattmeter, it is essential that the line current $i = I_m \cos(\omega t + \phi)$ flowing through the magnetizing solenoid, shown in Figure 8.1a, and the voltage $v = V_m \cos \omega t$ provide a Hall output voltage of the form

$$v_h = K_1 [V_m I_m \cos\phi + V_m I_m \cos(2\omega t + \phi)] . \tag{8.1}$$

K_1 is a constant of proportionality which includes the Hall coefficient and the proportionality between B and i. The first term on the right-hand side of Equation (8.1) is a d.c. voltage proportional to the power dissipated in the load resistance. In practice error terms [136], in addition to those normally encountered in Hall multipliers, appear owing to phase shift between the voltage in the transformer and the current in the magnetizing solenoid. This phase shift must be corrected if the d.c. term in Equation (8.1) is to be a true indication of dissipated (real) power.

A single-phase circuit for measuring [138, 139] the reactive power (VAR) is shown in Figure 8.1b. The sinusoidal magnetic induction is in phase quadrature with the Hall current

$$i = C_1 I_m \sin(\omega t + \phi)$$
$$B = C_2 V_m \sin(\omega t + \tfrac{1}{2}\pi) . \tag{8.2}$$

The constant of proportionality C_1 depends on the shunt resistance R_s as well as r, while C_2 represents the inherent proportionality required of the magnetic circuit. The Hall voltage of the circuit shown in Figure 8.1b is

$$v_h = K_2 V_m I_m [\cos(\phi - \tfrac{1}{2}\pi) - \cos(2\omega t + \phi + \tfrac{1}{2}\pi)] . \tag{8.3}$$

The first term on the right-hand side of Equation (8.3) is d.c. and is proportional to the reactive power in the circuit. A simple circuit for obtaining the right phase relationship for measuring reactive power is shown [141] in Figure 8.1c; capacitors are used to obtain the $\tfrac{1}{2}\pi$ phase shift and are so chosen that the input current to the Hall generator does not exceed its rated specifications. The output signal may be either positive or negative, depending on whether the reactive load appears as a capacitive or an inductive reactance. It is also possible to measure the virtual power (the product of the peak current and voltage) by means of a

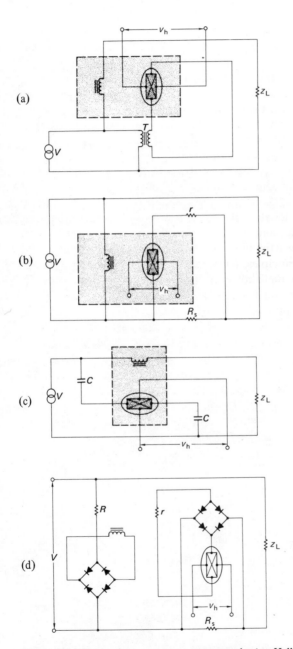

Figure 8.1. Single-phase a.c. wattmeters employing Hall generators: (a) Hall multiplier is in dash-enclosed rectangle and v_h is proportional to power dissipated in load impedance z_L; (b) wattmeter circuit without coupling transformer at the expense of power dissipated in series resistor R_s; (c) wattmeter circuit used for measuring reactive power; (d) diode rectification included to supply d.c. current and magnetic induction to Hall generator, avoiding phase-shift errors.

circuit such as shown in Figure 8.1d. The sinusoidal a.c. input is rectified by the bridge rectifiers and the input current to the Hall generator and the m.m.f. supplied to the magnetizing solenoid are proportional, respectively, to V_m and I_m.

Hall effect power transducers may also be used to determine the power distribution in a three-phase system [137] such as normally employed for a.c. line frequencies. Figure 8.2 represents schematically such a three-phase wattmeter. The input terminals of the three Hall generators are referenced to ground by means of the large bypass capacitors C. The series resistors R must satisfy the condition $\omega RC \gg 1$ in order that the input currents to the Hall generators be in phase with the corresponding voltages of the three-phase system. The output terminals of the three Hall generators are connected in series, and the sum of the Hall output voltages is proportional to the (real) power dissipated in the three load impedances Z_a, Z_b, and Z_c.

Hall generator wattmeters for the audio-frequency range, based on the above-described principles, have been described by Barlow [136] and subsequently by Kanellakos *et al.* [140]. An indium antimonide Hall generator, mounted on the center leg of a ferrite cup core in series with its solenoid, was employed for the construction of a wattmeter having a range of 0 to 0·4 W over a frequency range of 0·1 to 6 kHz and an impedance of 600 ohm. The frequency error was less than ±3·5% for unity power factor.

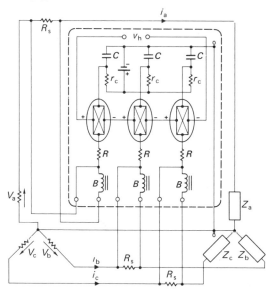

Figure 8.2. Three-phase a.c. wattmeter for measuring power dissipated in load impedances Z_a, Z_b, and Z_c; electrolytic capacitors C are providing polarizing voltages by means of resistors r_c; to avoid phase shifts between currents and voltages $\omega RC \gg 1$ (after Strutt [139]).

The measurement of high-frequency power in transmission lines or of microwave power in waveguides can be effected by means of Hall generators. If a Hall plate is placed at the center of a rectangular X-band waveguide excited in the TE_{01} mode, then the instantaneous electric field $\bar{e}$ produces in the Hall plate an instantaneous current $\bar{i}$ collinear with $\bar{e}$. Provided that the current and the instantaneous magnetic field $\bar{b}$ produced by the electromagnetic field have a uniform distribution over the cross section of the Hall plate, an instantaneous voltage $\bar{v}$ is present such that

$$v_h = \frac{R_h}{d} |\bar{i} \times \bar{b}| , \tag{8.4}$$

and the time average of this Hall voltage $\langle v_h \rangle$ is

$$\langle v_h \rangle = R_e \left(\frac{R_h}{d} i \times \bar{B}^* \right) \tag{8.5}$$

where B^* is the complex conjugate of the magnetic induction. The Poynting vector of the power flux density is $\bar{S} = \bar{E} \times \bar{H}$ and its time average is $\langle S \rangle = R_e |E \times H^*|$, where H^* is the complex conjugate of H.

In a waveguide in which the dominant mode is TE_{10}, the electric and magnetic fields are mutually perpendicular. In a Cartesian system the electric field E has a y component only, which is in phase with the x component of the magnetic field H. The magnetic field also has a z component, which is out of phase by $\frac{1}{2}\pi$ with respect to E. The time-averaged Hall voltage is directly proportional to the x component of the Poynting vector S_x, and

$$\langle v_h \rangle = K_3 E_y H_z [\cos \Delta\phi - \cos(2\omega t + \phi)] , \tag{8.6}$$

where K_3 is a constant of proportionality determined by the parameters of the Hall plate as well as by the propagation coefficients in the waveguide, and $\Delta\phi$ is the phase difference between E_y and H_z.

Barlow and Kataoka [142] investigated the behavior of a transmission-type wattmeter based on this principle. At 10 GHz, using a germanium Hall plate, they obtained a fair proportionality between the d.c. Hall voltage and the power in the waveguide, determined independently by means of a calorimeter, for power levels below 1 W. At higher power levels, the temperature distribution within the Hall plate is inhomogenous. Furthermore, the reflection coefficient presented by the Hall plate to the waveguide is not necessarily the same for power flow forward and in the reverse direction. The temperature of the face of the Hall plate on which the wave is incident is slightly higher than the obverse side. A serious problem of transmission-type wattmeters is the high electric field in the Hall plate; E is usually about 500 times larger than H. These problems can be circumvented to some extent by using a directional coupler between the waveguide and the wattmeter, by modulating the power transmitted along the guide at some suitably high frequency (~3 kHz), so that the thermal response is eliminated from $\langle v_h \rangle$, and by recording $\langle v_h \rangle$ after its passage through a narrow-band amplifier. Rotating the Hall plate about the H axis of the waveguide, a condition can be found such that a linear relation is obtained between the power level and the Hall voltage output.

A transmission-type wattmeter using an $InAs_{0.8}P_{0.2}$ Hall generator for measuring continuous-wave power in the microwave S-band ranges from 0 to 250 W was described by Rugari [143]. The device was mounted in the waveguide close to the side walls. The standing-wave ratio was measured to be 1·06 before inserting the Hall generator and 1·08 after mounting. A d.c. Hall voltage of 0·733 μV was found to correspond to 1 W of power in the guide, measured against a calorimeter power meter. The d.c. Hall voltage was found to have a linear dependence on power, up to 0·22 kW, with an accuracy of the order of ±5% and no apparent drift over a period of 8 hours.

A simpler and, in many respects, more advantageous method of power measurement in the microwave spectrum was developed by Barlow and Stephenson [144, 145]. A resonant H_{01} cavity, about one wavelength long, in which the Hall plate is mounted, is coupled magnetically to the main waveguide carrying the power to be measured. Figure 8.3 shows the Hall plate at the center of such a cavity, where the magnetic field is a maximum and the electric field is zero. A small current is fed to the Hall plate from the main waveguide by means of a probe projecting through a coupling slot. This current is nearly in time quadrature with the E field in the main guide, and the H field in the resonant cavity is likewise almost in quadrature with the H field in that guide. Tuning screws are provided to adjust the phase relationships in the resonant cavity for a maximum d.c. output $\langle v_h \rangle$. A prototype instrument built by Stephenson and Barlow [145] had a tuning range of 30 MHz about a

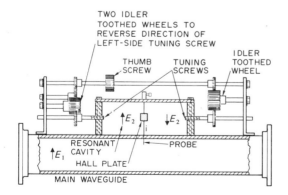

Figure 8.3. Resonant cavity-type microwave wattmeter based on Hall effect (after Stephenson and Barlow [145]).

center frequency of $4 \cdot 22$ GHz and a sensitivity of $22 \cdot 3$ μV W^{-1} ± 3% for a standing-wave ratio between $1 \cdot 0$ and $0 \cdot 1$. It was found to be linear in $\langle v_{\mathrm{h}} \rangle$ between 0 and $0 \cdot 22$ W, and estimates suggest that the instrument can be used up to 20 W without overheating the Hall plate.

Magnetoresistors employed in squaring multiplier circuits [146, 121, 147] can be used for the construction of single-phase or polyphase wattmeters. A typical circuit is shown in Figure 8.4. A permanent magnet or an auxiliary d.c. electromagnet is used for biasing a magnetoresistor into its linear $R(B)$ versus B range. The resistors R_1 and R_2 are so chosen that the current $I_{\mathrm{m}} \sin(\omega t + \phi)$ is independent of $R(B)$, a condition met by making $R_2 \gg R(B)$. Just as for the Hall generator wattmeters, the a.c. magnetic induction must be proportional to the input current and in phase with the voltage if the real power dissipated in Z_{L} is to be measured. Phase-shifting the current with respect to the voltage by $\frac{1}{2}\pi$ can be used for measuring reactive power. The potential across the magnetoresistor circuit contains three components: a d.c. component, one with the angular frequency ω, and another with an angular frequency 2ω. Provided that the power dissipated by $R(B)$, R_1, and R_2 is negligible with respect to that dissipated by Z_{L}, the d.c. potential developed across R_1 and R_2 is proportional to the real power in Z_{L}. The capacitor C in Figure 8.4 is used to block this d.c. voltage from completing the circuit through $R(B)$, and is chosen so that $R_2 \omega C \gg 1$ in order that no undesirable phase shifts be introduced by its presence in the circuit.

The power in multiphase power [146] lines having one grounded conductor may be determined by means of wattmeters such as shown in Figure 8.4. One unit per phase is required, and the sum of the d.c. voltages developed across the respective magnetoresistors represents the total power in the multiphase system.

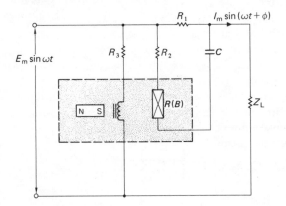

Figure 8.4. Wattmeter employing magnetoresistors for measuring real or reactive power in Z_{L}; a permanent magnet is used to bias magnetoresistor into its linear $R(B)$ versus B range and R_{s} corrects the phase shift produced by the magnetizing solenoid.

Raster pattern magnetoresistors suitably biased with a d.c. magnetic field ($\sim$3·5 kG to 5 kG) can also be used as wattmeters in the microwave spectrum in a manner analogous to that employed for Hall-effect microwave wattmeters. Kataoka [148, 149] and Kataoka and Naito [150] have described the design construction and performance of transmission-type wattmeters with a sensitivity of $\sim$3 μV W^{-1}, and resonant cavity-type wattmeters with a much higher sensitivity of $\sim$0·1 mV W^{-1}.

A comparison of Hall-effect and magnetoresistance wattmeters suggests the following conclusions: (1) the phase balancing is simpler for magneto-resistance devices than for Hall generators and an extended frequency response is obtainable with the former; (2) thermoelectric error voltages due to thermal gradients are of much smaller significance in magnetoresistors than in Hall generators; (3) the output signals of magnetoresistance wattmeters are much larger than those of Hall generator wattmeters.

Hall generators and magnetoresistors can also be used for measuring the root-mean-square (r.m.s.) value of a time-varying current in a circuit. The r.m.s. current I_{rms} is defined in terms of a constant current which produces the same heat dissipation:

$$I_{rms} = \left[\frac{1}{T} \int_0^T i^2(t)\,dt \right]^{\frac{1}{2}}. \tag{8.7}$$

Figure 8.5a represents a circuit suitable for measuring experimentally I_{rms} by means of Hall generators. Let the current to be measured $i(t)$ have a sinusoidal character with an angular frequency ω, and let it be applied to Hall generator No.1. The output voltage of the latter is then

$$v_{h1} = K_1 I_m^2 \sin^2 \omega t = \tfrac{1}{2} I_m^2 (1 + \cos 2\omega t), \tag{8.8}$$

where K_1 is a constant of proportionality between $i(t)$ and the magnetic induction as well as the parameters of the Hall generator. Hall generator No.2 is driven by a d.c. input current whose polarity and magnitude are so chosen that the differential voltmeter can produce a null against the d.c. component of v_{h1}. It is readily apparent that, if the d.c. component of v_{h1} is equal to v_{h2}, then the r.m.s. value of the a.c. current is equal to the magnitude of the d.c. current. For high-precision measurements, the circuit shown in Figure 8.5b is more suitable. It shows that the d.c. and a.c. input currents flow in the same direction through the magnetizing solenoid and in opposite directions through the Hall generator. The net current flow through the latter is

$$(i_{dc} + I_m \sin \omega t)(i_{dc} - I_m \sin \omega t) = i_{dc}^2 - i_m^2 \sin^2 \omega t, \tag{8.9}$$

which can be written in the form

$$i_{dc}^2 - \tfrac{1}{2} I_m^2 + \tfrac{1}{2} I_m^2 \cos 2\omega t. \tag{8.10}$$

The Hall output voltage has no d.c. component if the r.m.s. value of the alternating current is equal to the amplitude of i_{dc}, as shown by Rehm [151].

Magnetoresistors may also be used for measuring the r.m.s. value of arbitrary time-varying functions, as shown by Epstein and Greenstein [152]. The square-law $R(B)$ versus B^2 characteristic of a Corbino disc or raster pattern magnetoresistor can be used as the basis for obtaining the quadratic response of an input signal applied to a magnetic circuit whose magnetic induction is a linear function of the magnetizing current applied to its solenoid. After integration by means of an integrating amplifier, the output signal of the magnetoresistance squaring unit might then be applied to a square-root computer such as shown in Figure 7.10 in order to calculate the r.m.s. current in accordance with Equation (8.7).

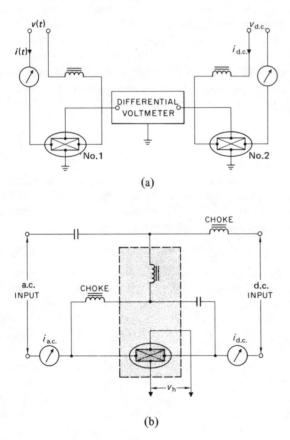

Figure 8.5. Circuit used to measure root-mean-square value of a current $i(t)$:
(a) differential method employing two Hall generators; (b) single Hall generator circuit.

Torque measurements

The mechanical torque T produced by a d.c. motor is proportional to the product of the magnetic flux generated by its stator and the current i fed to its rotor, $T = c_1 \phi i$. The magnetic flux ϕ in the air gap between stator and rotor may be considered as proportional to the magnetic induction of the stator pole pieces and c_1 as a constant of proportionality. If a Hall generator whose input current is proportional to the rotor current is placed in the air gap of a d.c. motor upon one of its stator pole pieces, as shown in Figure 9.1, then its Hall voltage v_h can be made to be proportional to the total torque [153, 154] of the motor:

$$T = c_2 v_h \; . \tag{9.1}$$

The total torque can be considered to be the sum of the real torque T_x available for performing external work and the torque T_i which represents the inherent losses (including frictional, copper, and iron losses) of the motor:

$$c_2 v_h = T_x + T_i \; . \tag{9.2}$$

Equation (9.2) suggests a linear dependence of v_h on the externally-measured torque (loading of the motor), with T_i determined from the intercept on the v_h axis for the unloaded ($T_x = 0$) motor. This has been ascertained experimentally [153]. The torque of a.c. motors may be determined by an analogous procedure [155] and the relation

$$T = c_3 (i_A \phi_B - i_B \phi_A) , \tag{9.3}$$

where c_3 is a coefficient of proportionality and i_A and i_B are the instantaneous currents in phases A and B, respectively; ϕ_A and ϕ_B are the

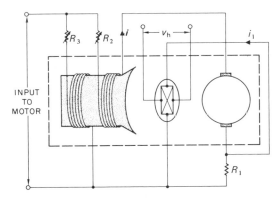

Figure 9.1. Torquemeter employing Hall generator mounted in air gap of d.c. motor; R_2 and R_3 are, respectively, current-limiting and control potentiometers which determine power in stator and stator–rotor circuit [153, 154].

instantaneous values of magnetic fluxes produced by phases A and B. Hall generators are placed symmetrically in the air gap on the stator along longitudinal (magnetic) axes of the corresponding phases. The number of Hall generators required is determined by the need to exclude the higher harmonics of the rotating magnetic field and also by the solenoid winding sections of the rotor.

Hall generators and magnetoresistors may also be used to advantage for probing the inhomogenous [156, 157] field distribution in the air gaps of slotted configuration d.c. motors and synchronous generators and motors. The static flux distribution as well as dynamic processes, such as commutation and switching, can be investigated in this manner. Vibrations in motors caused by intermittent coil failures can be determined and identified as shown by Hollitscher [158]. A Hall generator is placed in the air gap between stator and rotor, and the dynamic flux pattern is monitored on an oscilloscope. The scope is synchronized with the speed of the motor, and a stroboscopic technique is employed to pinpoint the defective coil without having to dismantle the machine searching for the breakdown point. Hall generators and magnetoresistors may also be used for the control and regulation of d.c. motors. The potentials developed during commutation are a function of the product of the rotor current i and of its speed of rotation n. If the current applied to the motor is at its maximum, then an increase in speed is permissible only if the rotor current is reduced commensurately, i.e. $(in)_{max} = $ const. This is readily accomplished by means of a circuit such as shown in Figure 9.2. The rotor current is applied to a current transducer in whose air gap is a Hall generator, the input current of which is a function of the motor speed [154]. A feedback loop can be used to control the current of the motor. Hall generators may also be used to limit the torque loading of a motor. The Hall output of a probe, mounted in the air gap of a motor in order to determine its torque, is connected to a sensitive relay disconnecting the rotor from its current source at a preselected voltage threshold level [153].

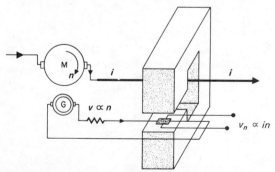

Figure 9.2. Control and regulation of a d.c. motor M by means of a Hall generator [154]; G is a motor generator coupled to M, whose output voltage V is proportional to velocity of rotation n of M.

Mechanical displacement transducers

Hall generators or magnetoresistors can be incorporated in transducers used for measuring the rectilinear or rotational displacement of an object from a specified reference position. For this purpose, a source of magnetic flux, such as a small permanent magnet, is attached to the object and a Hall generator or magnetoresistance bridge circuit is used to measure its magnetic field along a specified gradient. The spatial distribution of magnetic flux of a spherical dipole or bar magnet is, in terms of Figure 6.6 and Equation (6.10),

$$H_z = \frac{3M}{r^3}\cos\theta\sin\theta$$

$$H_\theta = \frac{M}{r^3}\sin\theta \ . \tag{10.1}$$

If the magnet is displaced along a direction which is parallel to one of the coordinate axes, say the z axis, then it is more convenient to express the z component of the magnetic field in Cartesian coordinates:

$$\frac{H_z}{3M} = \frac{xz}{(x^2+z^2)^{5/2}} \ . \tag{10.2}$$

Figure 10.1 shows this relation in graphical form and represents the dependence of $H_z/3M$ on the independent variable z for two specific parameters $x = 1$ and $x = 2$. The function $H_z(z)$ is strongly nonlinear, except over a relatively restricted range, $z \leqslant |0\cdot25|$. For applications which require displacement measurements over an extended linear range,

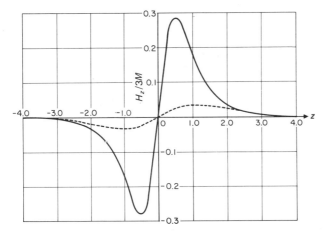

Figure 10.1. Normalized magnetic field in terms of magnetic moment of a dipole as a function of position along one coordinate z with x as a parameter [Equation (10.2)]; solid curve, $x = 1$; dashed curve, $x = 2$.

other magnetic circuit configurations are more suitable. These are described in Section 10.1.

Hall generators and magnetoresistors can also be used in conjunction with mechanically-displaceable flux sources as proximity switches or actuators. A relative displacement of sensor to source can be used to provide a signal which depends only on the sign, but not on the amplitude of the magnetic field. Alternatively, it can be triggered above a threshold amplitude of the magnetic field irrespective of its sign, or by a sign inversion at a specific position in space.

The angular transducers described in Section 10.2 employ Hall generators or magnetoresistors for producing an analog or digital output signal which represents the angle of rotation of a radially-magnetized permanent magnet rotor with respect to a reference plane. One of the principal advantages of such transducers in comparison with wire-wound synchros and resolvers based on electrodynamic principles is the elimination of rotor windings, slip rings, and brushes of the latter. The wire-wound transducers are, in fact, polyphase transformers whose mutual inductance coupling is a function of the electrical phase angle between stator and rotor.

Hall generators and magnetoresistors can also be used as commutators in small brushless d.c. motors having permanent magnet rotors. Section 10.3 deals with the construction, design, and operation of such motors. Hall generators or magnetoresistors are disposed in specific sectors of the air gap between stator and rotor and sense the relative position of the magnetic dipole which constitutes the rotor. They provide the commutation of the stator current to appropriate sector solenoids to start and maintain the rotation of the rotor and to control its speed with high accuracy.

10.1 Rectilinear displacement transducers

The rectilinear displacement of an object along a path may be determined by measuring the corresponding position-dependent magnetic field of a fixed magnet; a Hall generator is attached rigidly to the object and its Hall voltage is calibrated in terms of its mechanical displacement from a fixed reference position[1]. One of the principal considerations in the design of such transducers is the choice of an appropriate magnetic field gradient. A linear displacement transducer requires a constant gradient and a linear Hall generator or magnetoresistance bridge circuit. Figure 10.2 shows the experimentally-measured dependence of the magnetic induction on the distance away from the pole pieces of a permanent magnet, whose

[1] Electroacoustic Hall displacement transducers can be used as microphones; Hall generators attached to diaphragms actuated by acoustic pressure variations move in constant magnetic field gradients and produce a Hall output signal proportional to the acoustic amplitude. They can also be used as phonograph pickups for playback of lateral-type or depth-type grooved records (Wiehl, K., 1962, US Patent 3 046 361, issued 24 July 1962).

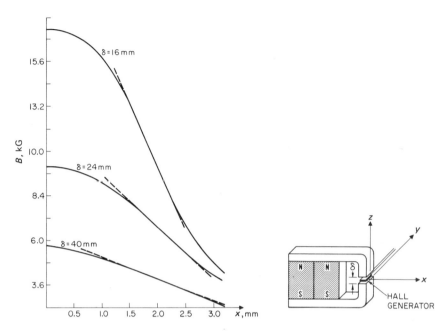

Figure 10.2 Magnetic induction as a function of displacement of a Hall generator in the air gap, between the pole pieces of a permanent magnet with different air gap lengths.

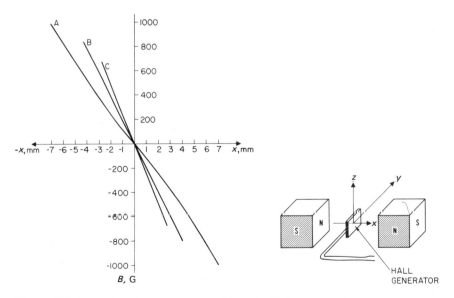

Figure 10.3 Magnetic induction versus position of a Hall generator between two magnets with their poles in flux opposition [159]; curves A, B, and C have gradients $\partial B/\partial x$ of 120 G mm^{-1}, 200 G mm^{-1}, and 240 G mm^{-1}, respectively.

parameters determine the transfer function $B(x)$. The data were obtained by means of a linear Hall generator displaced along the coordinate x. The linear v_h versus x range is a function of the magnetic induction in the air gap and fringing fields, and is restricted to ~0·2 cm. It can be extended [159, 160] to cover a wider range of ~±0·4 cm by using two permanent magnets with their poles in flux opposition, as shown in Figure 10.3. However, the magnetic field gradient dB/dx is about one order of magnitude smaller than that of the configuration shown in Figure 10.2, and consequently the resolution dv_h/dx of the Hall generator is commensurately smaller. The magnetic circuit shown in Figure 10.4 has a more restricted linear range: ±0·1 cm. Its advantage is a high linearity, a high magnetic field gradient comparable with that of the configuration shown in Figure 10.2, and a null in magnetic induction and consequently in v_h in the steady-state (no displacement) condition. Magnetic quadrupoles provide a linear $B(x)$ range considerably larger in extent than magnetic dipoles. Quadrupole electromagnets [161] with hyperbolically-shaped pole pieces can be made to have a constant axial magnetic gradient of the order of cm. Magnetostatic quadrupoles can be built, as shown in Figure 10.5, of four principal permanent magnets disposed symmetrically [162], and four smaller shimming magnets used to adjust the hyperbolic flux configuration between the principal magnets.

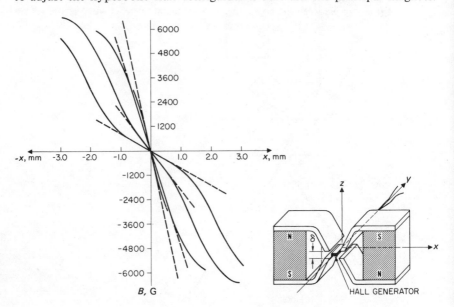

Figure 10.4. Magnetic induction as a function of rectilinear displacement [159]; linear portions of curves correspond to gradients of 0·84 kG mm^{-1}, 1·95 kG mm^{-1}, and 6·8 mG mm^{-1}, respectively, and depend on spacing between magnets with fixed $\delta = 1·6$ mm.

Jagger and Riley [162] obtained a field gradient of 470 G cm^{-1} across a 7·94 cm aperture magnetostatic quadrupole, such as shown in Figure 10.5, using ceramic permanent magnets with flat pole faces.

The construction and performance of a linear Hall displacement transducer in a magnetic feedback loop and in various magnetic circuit configurations have been analyzed by Nalecz and Warsza [163]. The Hall voltage of a linearized Hall generator $v_h = \gamma_B Bi$ is a function of the static magnetic field sensitivity γ_B, of the input current i_1, and of the magnetic induction B, presumed to have a dependence on the coordinate x, $B = f(x)$, and, consequently,

$$v_h = \gamma_B i_1 f(x) . \tag{10.3}$$

The voltage sensitivity of a rectilinear displacement transducer employing a Hall generator can be defined in terms of the magnetic field gradient $\partial B/\partial x$ as

$$\frac{dv_h}{dx} = \gamma_B i_1 \frac{\partial B}{\partial x} . \tag{10.4}$$

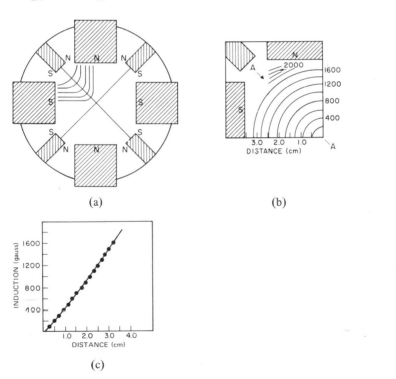

(a)

(b)

(c)

Figure 10.5. Quadrupole magnetic circuit for extending linear B versus displacement range: (a) principal magnets and auxiliary shimming magnets; (b) magnetic induction in one quadrant; (c) magnetic induction as a function of position along A-A axis shown in (b).

For a magnetic circuit configuration such as that shown in Figure 10.4, with $\partial B/\partial x = 10$ kG mm^{-1} and $\gamma_B i_{max} = 50$ mV kG^{-1}, Nalecz and Warsza [163] obtained a voltage sensitivity $dv_h/dx = 0.5$ V mm^{-1}, with an overall accuracy of $\sim 1.5\%$. A considerable improvement in resolution and accuracy of either linear or nonlinear displacement transducers can be realized by means of degenerative feedback. A Hall generator is used to measure the position-dependent magnetic induction along its displacement. The magnetic induction consists of an open-loop field $B_1 = f_1(x)$ and of a superposed field $B_2 = f_2(x)$, produced by the negative feedback loop of the circuit shown schematically in Figure 10.6. The magnetic induction $f_1(x)$, which may be produced by permanent magnets, induces a transverse Hall voltage v_h in the Hall generator, whose output is applied in turn to the amplifier with gain A and with a resultant output current i_o. A fraction β of the output current is applied to a magnetizing solenoid which produces the magnetic induction vector B_2. The negative feedback loop acting on the Hall generator constrains $B_1 = B_2$ in the steady state, and the transfer function of the circuit in Figure 10.6 is

$$\frac{i_o}{x} = -f_1(x)\frac{\gamma_B i_1 A}{1 + \beta\gamma_B i_1 A f_2(x)} . \tag{10.5}$$

If $\beta\gamma_B i_1 A f_2(x) \gg 1$, then Equation (10.5) becomes

$$i_o = -\frac{x}{\beta}\frac{f_1(x)}{f_2(x)} . \tag{10.6}$$

The output current i_o is thus a measure of the displacement x and depends on the local magnetic flux distributions. If the transducer is to have a linear dependence of its output signal on the displacement, then

$$\frac{f_1(x)}{f_2(x)} = kx , \tag{10.7}$$

where k is a constant of proportionality. The condition expressed by Equation (10.7) is satisfied if B_1 is a linear function of x and if the superposed feedback flux maintains the constancy of the total flux gradient. The relative error of such a transducer, derived from Equation (10.6), is

$$\delta i_o = -\delta f_1(x) + \delta f_2(x) + \delta\beta . \tag{10.8}$$

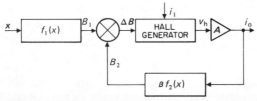

Figure 10.6. Principal components of Hall displacement transducer employing a closed feedback loop (after Nalecz and Warsza [163]).

The error depends on the stability of the amplifier and magnet, the constancy of the magnetic field gradients, and the uniformity of the field produced by the feedback solenoid. The circuit is to a large extent independent of thermal effects and other perturbations which affect the Hall generator and magnetic circuit. The Hall generator must have a high sensitivity, low residual misalignment voltage, and a high null-point stability. A linear displacement transducer built along the above-described principles [163] having a maximum displacement of $\pm 0 \cdot 5$ mm, produced a corresponding output $i_o = \pm 8 \cdot 5$ mA; its accuracy was found to be $\pm 1 \cdot 5\%$ full scale.

Rectilinear Hall generator displacement transducers can also be employed as seismometers [164] and as accelerometers [165]. The accelerometer system described by Nalecz and Ziomecki [165] consists of a mass m suspended from a flat spring forming a cantilever beam. The deflection of the beam due to a force acting on m is proportional to the acceleration. The deflection is measured by means of a Hall generator, attached rigidly to the free end of the spring, moving in a constant magnetic field gradient. Accelerations in the range between 10^{-4} g and 1 g have been measured in this manner.

Magnetoresistors can also be used as highly sensitive displacement transducers as shown by Ross and Saker [166]. Four identical magneto-resistor elements, preferably cut from the same InSb or InAs specimen, are arranged in a Wheatstone bridge circuit, as shown in Figure 10.7. The bridge is balanced in zero magnetic field. A small permanent magnet is used to produce a magnetic induction of $\sim$10 kG across a $0 \cdot 1$ cm air gap. With the magnet at the center of the Wheatstone bridge, so that the change in resistance of all four arms is the same, the bridge circuit maintains the balance and its output is null, just as in zero field. A vertical motion of the magnetoresistors relative to the magnet causes the resistance of one arm to increase, while that of the other arm decreases. Provided that the displacement is small, the output of the bridge circuit

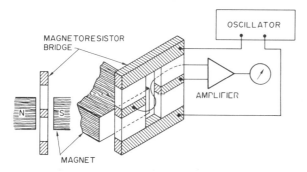

Figure 10.7. Displacement transducer based on magnetoresistor Wheatstone bridge in field of permanent magnet; hatched regions represent electrodes (after Ross and Saker [166]).

is then proportional to the displacement. Movements as small as 5 Å have been detected in this manner [28] and displacements of the order of 1 μm can be measured with relative ease. For a typical InSb transducer, the voltage sensitivity is ~0·5 V cm^{-1} and is linear over a range of ~0·05 cm.

A similar Wheatstone bridge displacement transducer was described by Yuan [167]. He used a single crystal of bulk sulfur-doped InSb, with a raster pattern of silver chemically plated and photolithographically processed to form a bridge circuit. A single magnetoresistor element is considered as the InSb region bounded by its two silver line electrodes (Section 5.1). The bridge circuit is displaced between the pole pieces of a magnet ($B \approx 12$ kG) in such a manner that, if both of the opposite arms R_1 and R_3 of the Wheatstone bridge increase in resistance by an equal amount ΔR, the other two arms R_2 and R_4 decrease in resistance by the same amount. The geometrical shape of a magnetoresistor has an effect upon the sensitivity of a displacement transducer and can be evaluated [167] with reference to Figure 10.8, which shows a magnetic induction acting on a fraction of a magnetoresistor, and by neglecting fringing fields. The displacement-dependent resistance $R(x)$ is

$$R(x) = \frac{l}{d}\left[\frac{x}{\rho(B)} + \frac{w-x}{\rho_0}\right]^{-1} , \qquad (10.9)$$

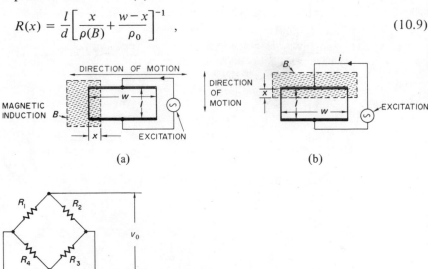

Figure 10.8. Rectilinear displacement transducer employing raster pattern magneto-resistors [167]: (a) transverse displacement; (b) longitudinal displacement; (c) magnetic field acts uniformly on Wheatstone bridge arms, producing equal incremental changes in R_1 and R_2 or R_3 and R_4.

provided that the direction of displacement is perpendicular to l. The corresponding magnetoresistance for this transverse case is

$$\left(\frac{\Delta R}{R_0}\right)_\perp = \frac{1}{R_0}[R(x) - R_0] \; ;$$

for

$$\frac{x}{w}\left[1 - \frac{\rho_0}{\rho(B)}\right] \ll 1 \; ,$$

Equation (10.9) becomes

$$\left(\frac{\Delta R}{R_0}\right)_\perp \approx \frac{x}{w}\left[1 - \frac{\rho_0}{\rho(B)}\right] \; . \tag{10.10}$$

If higher-order terms are negligible in Equation (10.10), then $(\Delta R/R_0)_\perp$ is proportional to the displacement x. A similar calculation made for a displacement longitudinal with respect to l leads to

$$\left(\frac{\Delta R}{R_0}\right)_\parallel \approx \frac{x}{l}\left[\frac{\rho(B)}{\rho_0 - 1}\right] \; , \tag{10.11}$$

which is also proportional to the displacement and is considerably larger than $(\Delta R/R_0)_\perp$, provided that $l \ll w$ and $\rho(B)/\rho_0 > 1$.

The sensitivity of a magnetoresistance displacement transducer was calculated by Williamson [168] for the case of a fixed magnetoresistor and a moving flux source having a gradient normal to the magnetoresistance element. He defined the magnetic field-dependent resistivity $\rho(B) = \rho_0(1 + CB^n)$, where the coefficient C depends on the material parameters and has a specific value in the square-law regime, where $n = 2$, and a different value in the high field region, where $n = 1$. The magnetic induction in the air gap of an electromagnet (the moving flux source) was defined as

$$B = Ni_m\left[x_a + \frac{x_m}{\mu_m}\right]^{-1} \; , \tag{10.12}$$

where N is the number of turns of the magnetizing solenoid, i_m is the magnetizing current, x_a the air-gap length, and x_m and μ_m are, respectively, the path length and the permeability of the magnetic circuit. The change in resistance per unit displacement of the flux source is

$$\left|\frac{dR}{dx}\right| = \frac{\Delta R}{R_0}\frac{R_0 n}{x_a + x_m/\mu_m} \; . \tag{10.13}$$

An experimental verification of this relation indicated the necessity of taking into account explicitly the magnetic fringing flux and leakage paths around the air gap. These alter Equation (10.12) and lead to a $|dR/dx|$ value which is smaller than that calculated by means of Equation (10.13).

Williamson [168] found good qualitative and fair quantitative agreement
between measured and calculated values of dR/dx and measured a maximum
sensitivity of $\sim 1 \cdot 1$ V cm^{-1}.

Rectilinear Hall and magnetoresistance displacement transducers can
be used as proximity switches for a variety of industrial machine-tool
operations, such as described in detail by Weiss [68]. As example is shown
in Figure 10.9. The fixed Hall generator or magnetoresistor bridge circuit
is mounted between two soft ferromagnetic pole pieces. The moving
E-shaped armature has a permanent magnet at its center, which generates
the return flux in the fixed assembly. Figure 10.9 shows the output
signals corresponding to various armature positions with respect to the
Hall or magnetoresistance probe. If the pole pieces have a rectangular
hysteresis loop, then the circuit can retain a 'memory' of its last operation,
or it can perform a binary-coded sequence of operations, provided that the
armature produces a field in excess of the coercivity of the pole pieces.
Such transducers are independent of the velocity of the armature and
essentially independent of environmental factors, such as dust, smoke, or
moderate temperature changes.

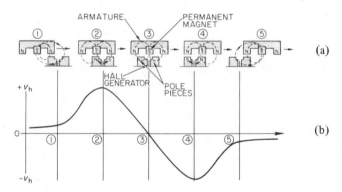

Figure 10.9. Magnetic displacement transducer: (a) magnetic circuit includes
permanent magnet, soft-iron pole pieces, and armature; also shown is position of Hall
generator; (b) output signal of Hall generator as a function of armature position.

10.2 Angular displacement transducers

Angular resolvers are electromechanical transducers, which develop an
output voltage proportional to an input voltage and to the sine (or cosine)
of the angle of rotation of their rotor with respect to a reference plane.
Resolvers can be used to perform a variety of analog computing functions,
such as rotation of coordinates, solution of plane and spherical triangles,
and similar trigonometric problems. Synchros are rotating devices
supplied by single-phase or polyphase power, whose output depends on
the phase, amplitude (or both) of the input, and on the position of its
rotor. The amplified output of such a synchro (transmitter) may be fed

to another similar device (a receiver), whose rotor position aligns itself in conformity with that of the transmitter. Conventional synchros and resolvers consist of a slotted wire-wound stator and a wire-wound rotor with a slip ring and brush assembly in a common housing. The slip rings and brushes degrade the performance and the reliability of such devices. Miniaturization is expensive and the frequency response of wire-wound resolvers and synchros is poor.

The main advantages of Hall and magnetoresistance synchros and resolvers is the elimination of all windings and brushes. The stator winding is replaced by two or more Hall generators or magnetoresistors, and an axially-rotating radially magnetized permanent magnet replaces the wire-wound rotor. Figure 10.10 represents schematically the structure of a Hall synchro [169–172]. Four Hall generators are disposed in radial

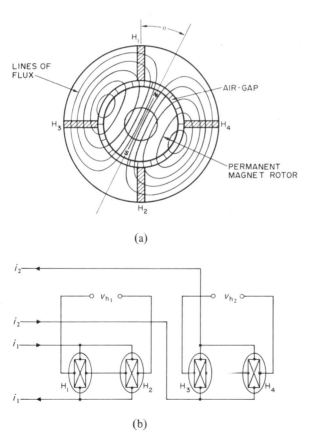

(a)

(b)

Figure 10.10. Diagram of a Hall synchro: (a) permanent magnet, radially magnetized rotor, and Hall generators H mounted in slots between highly-permeability stator sectors; (b) circuit interconnections of Hall generators; output signals are proportional, respectively, to $\sin\theta$ and $\cos\theta$.

slots of a high-permeability soft-ferromagnetic stator, and a cylindrical permanent magnet constitutes the rotor. For constant input currents to the Hall generators and $\theta = 0$, the magnetic flux acting on Hall generators H_1 and H_2, whose combined output signal is v_{h1}, is a maximum. The other two Hall generators H_3 and H_4 are in space quadrature, and their combined output $v_{h2} = 0$. Rotation of the rotor shaft produces a magnetic induction $B_0 \cos\theta$ acting on H_1 and H_2, and $B_0 \sin\theta$ correspondingly acting on H_3 and H_4. The resultant Hall output signals are therefore proportional, respectively, to the sine and cosine of the angle of rotation of the rotor with respect to the (electrical) zero plane of the resolver.

In practice, a number of problems are encountered in the implementation of such a simple Hall synchro. These include magnetic flux leakage in and around the air gaps, unequal flux distribution in the stator sectors, and inhomogeneity in the permanent magnet. Hysteresis effects in the stator return paths appear if the synchro is operated with d.c., and this gives rise to an operational error in excess of 2%. Hall synchros can be used as transmitters to drive conventional two-phase wire-wound synchro receivers. Donaldson [172] used such an arrangement shown in Figure 10.11. The transmitter consists of two Hall generators perpendicular to each other, driven by a common input current i_1 of 400 Hz. The output signals of the two Hall generators are proportional, respectively, to $\cos\theta$ and $\sin\theta$ and produce proportional flux components in the receiver. The output voltages induced in the rotor are proportional in turn to $\cos\theta \sin\phi$ and $\sin\theta \cos\phi$, respectively, and their sum is proportional to $\sin(\theta - \phi)$. This resultant signal is applied to a servoamplifier and motor connected to the shaft of the synchro receiver. In principle it drives the rotor to the steady-state condition in which its angular position is the same as that of the transmitter. In practice [172], the receiver was found to follow the transmitter only within $\pm 2 \cdot 5^\circ$. However, no dead zones were found and readings were repeatable to within $10'$. This indicates that the Hall synchro had a high signal-to-noise level and was free of hysteresis effects; however, a better distribution of stator reluctance rotor magnetization and symmetry might be needed to reduce the follow-up errors.

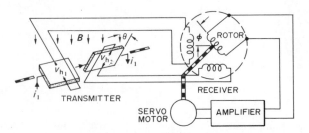

Figure 10.11. Hall synchro transmitter coupled to wire-wound synchro receiver (after Donaldson [172]).

A linear Hall synchro [173, 174] is an angular transducer whose output is a linear function of the angle θ through which its shaft is rotated, rather than of the sine or cosine of that angle. The problem which must be solved in order to obtain such a response is that of shaping the magnetic flux distribution of the rotor. This is usually accomplished by empirical procedures. The structure of a linear Hall synchro is shown in Figure 10.12. Two Hall generators, whose input currents are in series and may be either a.c. or d.c., provide a combined output signal which is a function of the integral of the angular magnetic flux density function on the inner surface of the stator return path. The magnetic induction must have a square-wave characteristic in order to obtain the triangular B versus θ relation shown in Figure 10.12. For this purpose, the rotor, usually of high-coercivity ferrite, must be fashioned in a specific shape, and the stator is chosen to have a high reluctance in order that the air gaps be tailored to fit the linear B versus θ function acting on the Hall generators. The high reluctance of the stator reduces the peak flux and lowers the resultant Hall output signals. Alternatively, a rectangular permanent magnet with semicylindrically shaped pole pieces, such as

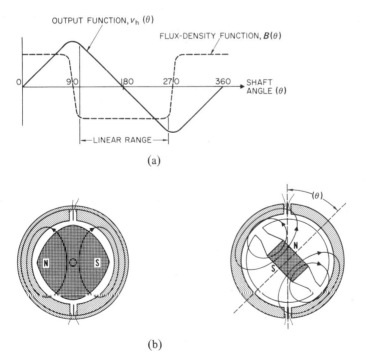

(a)

(b)

Figure 10.12. Linear Hall synchro: (a) output signal versus shaft angle θ, showing linear range; (b) shaped high-coercivity ferrite rotor used to obtain linear B versus θ dependence; rectangular permanent magnet rotor with shaped pole pieces for extended linear range.

shown in Figure 10.12, may be used as the rotor and the reluctance of the stator can be reduced to low values. Grancoin [174] reported a linearity error of the order of 0·2% for the latter type of linear synchro.

A disadvantage of using two or more Hall generators in angular transducers is the difficulty of insuring flux symmetry and homogeneity in the stator slots. Furthermore, since the Hall generator input circuits are coupled resistively to their output circuits through the Hall plates and misalignment-cancelling networks, the performance of the transducers is a function of magnetic flux, thermal perturbations, and input current. Davidson and Gourlay [175] approached the design of angular Hall transducers from a different viewpoint. They used a single fixed Hall generator as the stator mounted within the air gap of a shaped permanent magnet rotor arranged in accordance with Figure 10.13. The output of the Hall generator was applied to an integrated circuit amplifier by means of a matching transformer. Using 'Alnico' magnets and InAs Hall generators, they obtained a 5 V peak-to-peak output signal (into a 10 kΩ load) for a 28 V, 20 mA d.c. input. The resolver was 1·9 cm in diameter and 5·84 cm

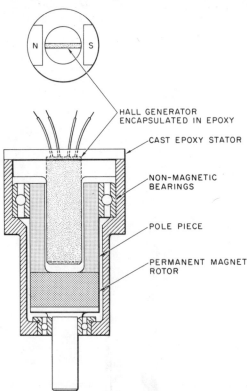

Figure 10.13. Angular resolver using a single fixed Hall generator surrounded by permanent magnet rotor (after Davidson and Gourlay [175]).

long. It had a 20' functional error at room temperature over a frequency range of 60 Hz to 20 kHz and a temperature stability of ±1·5% between −50°C and +90°C.

A different approach to the solution of the problem posed by the asymmetric flux distribution in Hall synchros was taken by Inglis and Donaldson [176]. They eliminated the slotted stator sectors and mounted the Hall generators in the air gap between a radially-magnetized cylindrical rotor and a concentric magnetic shield of soft iron or μ-metal. They solved the equations defining the radial and angular components of the magnetic induction in the annular air gap, and found that both are sine functions of the angular position of the rotor and that they are in space quadrature. For a rectangular Hall plate of length l and width w, the normal flux Φ_n acting upon it, in the air gap of Figure 10.14, can be defined in terms of the intensity of magnetization M of the rotor, the input current axis of the Hall generator $r_1\theta$, and the angle δ between the Hall plate and the radial plane containing this axis. Further, defining a normalized radius $R = r/b$ and a normalized width $W = w/b$, the output voltage of the Hall plate in terms of the parameters of Figure 10.14a is

$$v_h = R_h i_1 \frac{M}{2}\left(\frac{a}{b}\right)^2 \frac{\mu_0}{w} P\sin(\theta + \theta') , \qquad (10.14)$$

where the terms P and θ' are, respectively

$$P = \left\{4 + W^2 + \frac{W^2 + \frac{1}{4}W^4 - 4R^4}{[R^2 + (\frac{1}{2}W)^2]^2 - R^2 W^2 \cos^2\delta}\right\}^{\frac{1}{2}} \qquad (10.15)$$

$$\theta' = \tan^{-1}\left\{\cot\delta \frac{R^2 - (\frac{1}{2}W)^2 - [R^4 + (\frac{1}{2}W)^4 - 2R^2(\frac{1}{2}W)^2 \cos 2\delta]}{R^2 + (\frac{1}{2}W)^2 - [R^4 + (\frac{1}{4}W)^4 - 2R^2(\frac{1}{2}W)^2 \cos 2\delta]}\right\} . \qquad (10.15)$$

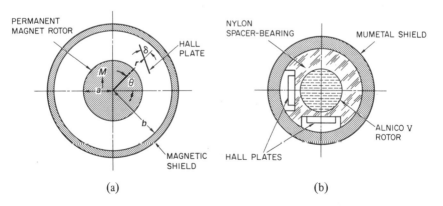

(a)   (b)

Figure 10.14. Magnetic flux distribution and construction of tangential Hall synchro: (a) Hall plate in air gap between permanent magnet rotor and magnetically-shielded enclosure; (b) sectional end elevation of a tangential synchro (after Inglis and Donaldson [176]).

If the Hall plate is in a tangential position with respect to the rotor, $\delta = \frac{1}{2}\pi, \frac{3}{2}\pi$, etc., and $(\frac{1}{2}W)^2 + (\frac{1}{2}W)^4 < R^4$, then P is a maximum with respect to δ,

$$P_t = \frac{W[1 + R^2 + (\frac{1}{2}W)^2]}{R^2 + (\frac{1}{2}W)^2} . \tag{10.16}$$

The boundary conditions: $(\frac{1}{2}W)^2 + (\frac{1}{4}W)^4 > R^4$ and δ an odd multiple of $\frac{1}{2}\pi$ lead to a maximum value of v_h for tangentially mounted Hall plates, such as shown in Figure 10.14b. Such a synchro system is more amenable to an overall reduction in size than one in which the Hall plates are disposed radially with respect to the rotor. Inglis and Donaldson have built and tested a number of such synchros using Alnico as well as Platinax permanent magnet rotors. A comparison of the theoretically predicted and experimentally measured angular and radial components of the magnetic induction and the parameters and variables of Equation (10.14) yielded favorable agreement. The substitution of such a Hall synchro for a conventional wire-wound two-phase synchro transmitter in a position-control servo system led to follow-up errors of the order of ±1° and a reading accuracy of ±0·1°. Miniature synchros of this type with an overall length of 2·5 cm and a diameter of ~1 cm, with a maximum phase output at 400 Hz of ~30 mV, were found to be capable of resolving angles to within a maximum electrical error of ±10'.

An incremental angle encoder is a shaft position to digital data transducer. Strandt [177] has described a Hall-effect incremental angle encoder which, if used in conjunction with a bidirectional counter, provides information in digital form about the angular position and rate of motion of a single track, ~4·6 cm diameter, magnetic drum. Two Hall generators spaced from each other by an integral number of π/n radians are required if the direction of rotation of the drum is also to be determined, and also to improve the resolution of the encoder.

Figure 10.15 represents a block diagram of the encoder. It consists of two microminiature InAs Hall generators arranged to measure the vertical component of the remanent magnetization of 1024 bits recorded on a nonreturn to zero (NRZ) clock track on the drum. The Hall generators, mounted 90° apart, were capable of resolving information stored at the rate ~71 bits cm^{-1}. They were driven by an a.c. input current of 10 mA and frequency of 40 kHz, $i_1 = i_0 \sin \omega_c t$. If the recorded magnetic flux with a positive polarity is defined as a binary '1' and that with a negative polarity is defined as a binary '0', then

$$v_{h1} = KBi_0 \sin \omega_c t \qquad \text{for a '1'}$$

$$v_{ho} = KBi_0 \sin (\omega_c t + \pi) \qquad \text{for a '0'} \tag{10.17}$$

represent the corresponding output signals in the Hall generators, i.e. their input currents are phase-modulated by the recorded binary information and the phase of the 40 kHz carrier is shifted by π in the case of a binary 'zero' with respect to a 'one' bit. The output from the encoder is a train of square waves displaced in phase by $\frac{1}{2}\pi$. These can be applied to a counter or accumulator to determine the angular rotation rate or position of the drum. The encoder was found to have an angular resolution within $11'$ of arc.

Rectilinear magnetoresistance displacement transducers, such as described in Section 10.1, are based on the dependence of the resistance of a magnetoresistor on the fraction of its volume immersed in a fixed magnetic field. Angular magnetoresistance transducers [178–181] can be produced in a similar manner. A magnetoresistor is mounted within the air gap of a magnetic circuit, and a cylindrical permanent magnet rotor is used to cover a variable fraction of its volume. In order to produce a required functional dependence of the resistance on the angular position of the rotor, the geometrical configuration of the magnetic circuit, of the magnetoresistor, or both of these, may be tailored to specific contours. Within the air gap the flux lines may be radial and at right angles to the axis of rotation of the rotor. The latter may have a worm shape, so arranged that its peripheral edge traverses the magnetoresistor surface along an axial direction. Alternatively, the direction of the flux in the air gap may be parallel to the axis of rotation of the rotor. The motion of the latter with respect to the magnetoresistor may be in the form of a planar spiral. A different rotor configuration suitable for producing a sinusoidal dependence of the resistance on the angle of rotation is that of

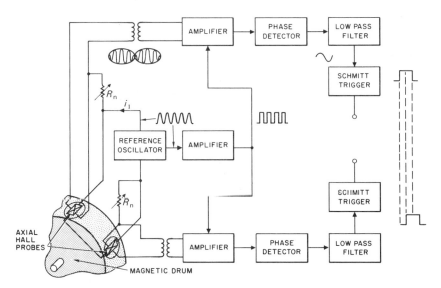

Figure 10.15. Incremental angle encoder employing Hall generators and magnetic recording drum (after Strandt [177]).

a circular disc slanted with respect to its axis of rotation, its outer peripheral edge being parallel to the cylindrical axis of a soft-ferromagnetic stator on which the magnetoresistor is mounted.

A high-accuracy angular resolver based on the same principles as the magnetoresistance multipliers and modulators, described in Sections 7.2 and 11.1, is shown in Figure 10.16. Two identical magnetoresistors are placed in opposite slots of two semicylindrical stator shells of μ-metal. Solenoid windings on each of the stator shells are driven by a 60 Hz or 400 Hz magnetization current i_{ac}. The permanent magnet rotor produces a steady magnetic flux B_s, whose value is added to the instantaneous a.c. flux in one of the stator shells and subtracted from the other. In the presence of the combination of a.c. and d.c. magnetic fluxes acting on the magnetoresistors $R(B)_1$ and $R(B)_2$, their instantaneous resistances are

$$R(B)_1 = R_0 [1 + k(B_s + B_{ac})^2]$$
$$R(B)_2 = R_0 [1 + k(B_s - B_{ac})^2] .$$

(10.18)

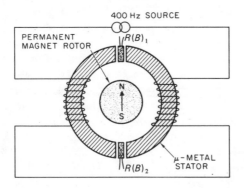

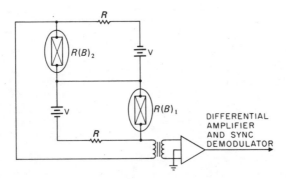

Figure 10.16. Angular resolver employing magnetoresistors; the effective flux is a combination of the alternating flux of stator superposed on steady angular position-dependent flux of the radially-magnetized rotor.

If a d.c. current is applied to the two magnetoresistors and the signals developed across them due to d.c. combined alternating and steady fluxes are subtracted from each other in a differential amplifier then, since $B_s = B_0 \sin\theta$, where θ is the angle of rotation of the rotor

$$v_0(\Delta R) = 4B_{ac}B_0 \sin\theta ,\qquad\qquad (10.19)$$

where $v_0(\Delta R)$ is the difference output signal. The differential output voltage is thus proportional to the angular position of the rotor with respect to a reference plane. Since only two magnetoresistors are shown in Figure 10.16, the range of the resolver is $+90°$ and $-90°$. Figure 10.17 (p.54ff.) shows the principal components of such a resolver. Synchronous detection of the output signal provides a resolution of $\pm 1'$ of arc between $0°$ and $180°$ and corresponding output signals of ± 10 mV d.c. full scale for maximum shaft positions of $\pm 90°$.

10.3 Brushless electric motors

In a conventional d.c. motor [182] the stator solenoids set up a magnetic field which has a stationary spatial distribution. The armature winding of the rotor has its own magnetic field due to current fed to its solenoids. The purpose of the brush and commutator assembly is to switch the current flowing to the armature in such manner that the axis of the rotor magnetic field is stationary in space at $90°$ with respect to that of the stator. If a permanent magnet is used as the rotor, then power need no longer be supplied to the armature through its slip rings or brushes. However, with the field poles rotating, the axis of the stator field must also rotate at the same speed as the rotor in order to maintain the spatial quadrature. For this purpose, information concerning the angular position of the rotor must be relayed to a switching network which controls the currents applied to the solenoids wound on the stator, so that the spatial phase of its field leads by $90°$ that of the rotor. Either the torque-producing permanent magnet rotor or an auxiliary commutating magnet attached rigidly to the rotor axis can provide the necessary signals induced in Hall generators or magnetoresistance transducers for detecting the angular position of the rotor.

A schematic representation of a brushless d.c. motor [183] employing Hall generators is shown in Figure 10.18. The angular position sensor consists of a permanent magnet commutator and a number of radially-disposed Hall generators, connected to coils placed in appropriate slots of the stator to produce the spatial phase quadrature between the torque-producing permanent magnet rotor and the stator fields. The rotor in trying to align itself with the stator field also rotates the commutating magnet, and thus changes the field acting on the Hall generators. As the rotor attempts to follow the stator field, whose magnitude and polarity is changing in time, it forces the stator field to rotate away from it. The

direction of rotation of the motor is a function of the polarity of the
input current to the Hall generators. Reversing the current reverses the
polarity of the Hall generator output voltages. This causes the motor to
slow down and eventually to reverse its direction of rotation. The
commutating magnet and the Hall generators thus replace the functions of
the commutator and brush assembly or slip rings of conventional d.c.
motors. The advantages of Hall generators for sensing the position of the
rotor, over electrodynamic transducers whose output depends on the time
rate of change of the magnetic flux, is that Hall generators can provide the
necessary current steering for starting the rotation of a motor from
standstill. Also the amplitudes of their outputs are independent of motor
speed. The Hall generators are used in conjunction with electronic
circuits, which provide the stator impulse currents. These circuits may
be driven in either of two modes: as power amplifiers of the Hall
generator output signals or as electronic switches triggered into conduction
by the Hall output signals. The amplifying mode is to be preferred if
smooth control of motor speed is required [2]. If a high efficiency is the
primary consideration, then the switching mode is more advantageous
[184, 185]. A typical motor, driven with 9 V d.c., develops a mechanical
power of 0·5 W with an efficiency of 56% at a speed of 5500 r.p.m.
[184].

Brushless d.c. motors, using Corbino disc magnetoresistors as angular
position sensors of the field of a dipole magnet commutator mounted on
the same axis as a torque-producing quadrupole permanent magnet rotor,
have been suggested by Quichaud and Bonnefille [186]. Four Corbino
discs mounted in stator slots along two perpendicular diameters of a

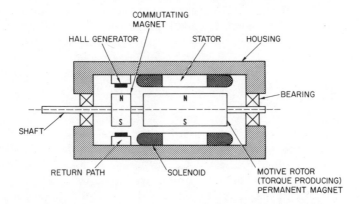

Figure 10.18. Brushless d.c. motor using Hall generators for commutation and steering
of currents in stator sectors.

(2) The amplifier output signal is a function of the flux of the commutating magnet
and the magnitude and polarity of the input currents to the Hall generators.

cylindrical stator cage are presumed to form a commutating four-pole circuit. The magnetic induction of the dipole magnet acts in sequence on alternate Corbino disc pairs, which switch the solenoid currents of the stator so as to maintain the rotation of the quadrupole rotor. The calculated efficiency of such a system is moderate; assuming identical magnetoresistors with $R(B) = R_0(1 + \mu_n^2 B^2)$, $B = 5$ kG, and $\mu_n \approx 8 \times 10^4$ cm^2 V^{-1} s^{-1}, the maximum attainable efficiency is ~37%.

A different motor structure employing field-plate magnetoresistors was described by Weiss [68, 77]. Three solenoids, each covering 120° sector, are wound on a cylindrical soft-ferromagnetic stator. A permanent magnet rotor, radially magnetized, acts on three field plates mounted on the stator and spaced radially at 120° from each other. The permanent magnet has a segment-shaped angular region, somewhat greater[3] than 120°, in which $B \approx 0$. At least one field-plate is in this field free region at any given time. The switching transistor in Figure 10.19 associated with this field plate is 'on' and current is supplied to the solenoid in its

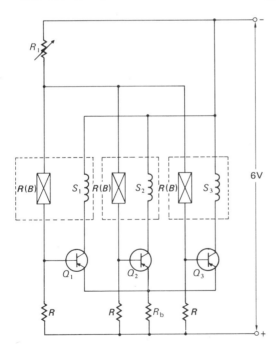

Figure 10.19. Brushless three-pole ma[g]netoresistor field-plate motor [after Weiss, H.. 1969, *Structure and Application of Galvanomagnetic Devices* (Pergamon Press, Oxford), p.331].

[3] About 125° to 140°; two rather than three magnetoresistors may be used provided that a NAND gate is incorporated [187] in the switching circuit and used in conjunction with the third sector solenoid of Figure 10.19.

load circuit. The other two transistors are 'cut-off' owing to the fact
that their magnetoresistors are in the magnetic field of the rotor;
consequently their high-resistance states produce the necessary cut-off
bias. The purpose of the series resistor R_1 is that of shaping the voltages
at the collector electrodes of the switching transistors. Without this
resistor, the collector voltages, and consequently the currents in the
solenoids, have a nearly square-wave shape dependence on the angle of
rotation of the rotor. The effect of R_1 is to produce a sinusoidal
dependence of the collector voltage on the angle of rotation; this also
improves the efficiency of the motor. Speed may be varied by varying
R_1, and can be regulated by replacing R_1 with a transistor, whose base is
driven by the potential difference derived from the rectified voltage across
one of the stator solenoids compared against a suitable reference such as
a Zener diode. Small (6·1 cm long and ~2·8 cm in diameter) field-plate
motors [68] built and used in accordance with this description, driven by
6 to 9 V d.c., have a maximum speed of 3000 r.p.m. and a maximum
torque of ~30 cmp. Their efficiency is of the order of 50%.

Communications and signal processing applications

Hall and magnetoresistance multipliers can be used to perform a variety of signal processing functions, such as modulation, detection, correlation, and spectrum analysis over a wide range of frequencies from the audio range up to and including microwaves. Unlike other electronic multipliers, which use the transfer characteristic of inherently nonlinear devices to perform multiplication, Hall multipliers and balanced magnetoresistance bridge circuits operate as linear multipliers. Their output is proportional to the product of two input variables, which may be quite different time-dependent synchronous or asynchronous functions, and their amplitudes may vary over wide dynamic ranges. These are the properties of primary interest for the signal processing applications described in the following sections.

11.1 Modulators and demodulators

Hall multipliers can be used as wide-band modulators in communication systems. If the input current $i_1 = i_0 \cos \omega_1 t$ to a Hall plate is considered as the carrier and the magnetic induction $B = B_0 \cos \omega_2 t$ is the superposed modulation, then the resultant Hall voltage is

$$v_h = \tfrac{1}{2} v_m [\cos(\omega_1 + \omega_2)t + \cos(\omega_1 - \omega_2)t] , \qquad (11.1)$$

where $v_m = i_0 B_0$. In principle, the carrier is suppressed, the modulator is balanced [188–190], and the output signal from the Hall generator contains only the two side bands $\omega_1 + \omega_2$ and $\omega_1 - \omega_2$. In practice, 'carrier breakthrough' from the input to the output circuit can occur owing to inductive coupling between them. The magnitude of this undesired voltage v_Q superposed on v_h is $v_Q = \pm j\omega_1 M i_1$, where M is the mutual inductance between the input and output circuits of the Hall generator. It may be reduced to a minimum by placing the output leads in a noninductive arrangement. The resistive coupling between the input and output circuits allows the compensation of v_Q, which is in phase quadrature with respect to i_1, by connecting a suitable capacitance[1] between the input and one of the output electrodes. Eddy currents in the Hall plate represent a negligible perturbation, provided that the air gap of the magnetic circuit is at least one order of magnitude greater than the Hall plate thicknesses. Capacitive coupling between the magnetizing solenoid, usually wound on a cup core of ferrite, and the Hall plate mounted on its center post can be suppressed by a Faraday shield between them [191]. Inductive coupling between them can be overcome by

---

[1] For frequencies between 0·35 MHz and 5 MHz a suitable capacitance is one in the range between 15 pF and 80 pF; a reduction of carrier breakthrough of −50 dB below v_h can be achieved [191] in this manner.

feeding to the output circuit of the Hall generator a voltage derived from a two-turn coil wound on the same core as the magnetizing solenoid. It must produce [192] a voltage equal in magnitude and opposite in phase to that induced in the output circuit. Figure 11.1 shows a Hall modulator [193] using a 1 MHz carrier modulated by 400 Hz. The carrier is impressed on the Hall generator rather than on the magnetic circuit due to high core losses of the magnetic material at 1 MHz. The magnetic circuit is operated in series resonance in order to minimize the input power at 400 Hz and the output signal is measured across a capacitive load of 15 pF across the Hall electrodes. Hilbinger [193] found that the output of such a modulator is linear[2] within 1% from zero to a peak magnetic excitation of ±12 ampere turns. He obtained an output of 100 V peak-to-peak with the circuit shown in Figure 11.1, using 0·85 W of carrier input power and a modulation of 12 ampere turns.

Hall generators may also be used for generating single side band (SSB) suppressed carrier signals, as shown by Epstein *et al.* [194] and Epstein and Brophy [195]. Suppose that a carrier signal $A \sin \omega_c t$ is applied to a Hall generator and a modulating signal

$$V(t) = \sum_{n=1}^{N} a_n \cos(\omega_n t + \phi_n) \tag{11.2}$$

is applied to its magnetizing solenoid. The output of the multiplier is

$$v_h(t)_1 = kA \sum_{n=1}^{N} a_n \cos(\omega_n t + \phi)\sin \omega_c t . \tag{11.3}$$

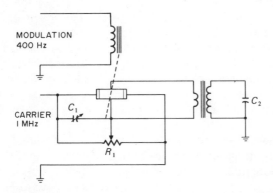

Figure 11.1. Balanced Hall modulator with capacitive loading and reactive circuit compensation.

[2] The harmonic distortion of open-circuited or lightly-loaded Hall modulators driven by sinusoidal input signals is of the order of 10^{-3}, and rises to about 10^{-2} for a matched load ($B \approx 1$ kG). The distortion is due to inherent nonlinearities in the Hall generator and magnetic circuit analyzed in terms of a six-pole (three-port) configuration (Gruetzman, S., 1965, *Frequenz,* **19**, 41).

Suppose that a second multiplier, identical with the first, has a modulation impressed upon it which is in phase quadrature with Equation (11.2):

$$V(t) = \sum_{n=1}^{N} b_n \sin(\omega_n t + \phi_n) , \qquad (11.4)$$

and its carrier signal is also shifted in phase by $90°$ with respect to that of the first multiplier, $B \cos \omega_c t$. The output voltage of the second Hall multiplier is then

$$v_h(t)_2 = kB \sum_{n=1}^{N} b_n \sin(\omega_n t + \phi) \cos \omega_c t . \qquad (11.5)$$

If $Aa_n = Bb_n$ for all values of ω, then adding or subtracting the outputs of the two multipliers leads to a single side-band output of the form

$$kA \sum_{n=1}^{N} a_n \sin[(\omega_c + \omega_n)t + \phi_n] , \qquad (11.6a)$$

or that of the other side band

$$kA \sum_{n=1}^{N} a_n \sin[(\omega_c - \omega_n)t + \phi_n] . \qquad (11.6b)$$

A method of suppressing one of the side bands [195] in an SSB system employing Hall generators is illustrated in Figure 11.2.

Phase modulation of sinusoidal signals [194, 195] can be effected by introducing the carrier and modulating signals in a balanced modulator employing a Hall multiplier. The output of the modulator is then added to a quadrature component of the original carrier. The phase of the combined signal has a linear dependence on the modulation provided that the quadrature signal is at least twice as large as the output of the balanced modulator. The major advantage of such a phase modulation scheme is its frequency stability. Epstein and Brophy [195] have described the construction and performance of such phase modulators. For a phase modulation index of $m \leqslant 0·5$ the amplitude modulation did not exceed 6% and was periodic at the first harmonic of the modulation frequency.

Hall generators may also be used as linear phase-sensitive demodulators and detectors [189, 190]. Figure 11.3 represents such a detector, composed of two identical Hall multipliers driven in phase quadrature. The input current of the first Hall generator is $i_1 = i_1' \sin(\omega t + \phi)$, and its magnetizing current is $i_m = I_1 \cos \omega t$; ϕ is the phase angle between i_1 and i_m. The output voltage of the first multiplier is

$$v_{h1} = \tfrac{1}{2} k_1 I_1 i_1'[\sin(2\omega t + \phi) + \sin \phi] . \qquad (11.7)$$

In addition to the second harmonic component, the output contains a d.c. term proportional to the phase angle ϕ. The second Hall multiplier in Figure 11.3 has its input current $i_2 = i_2' \cos(\omega t + \phi)$ shifted in phase by

$\frac{1}{2}\pi$ with respect to i_1. Its magnetizing current $i'_m = I_2 \sin \omega t$ is also shifted in phase with respect to i_m by $\frac{1}{2}\pi$, and its output is

$$v_{h2} = \tfrac{1}{2} k_2 I_2 i'_2 [\sin(2\omega t + \phi) - \sin \phi] \ . \tag{11.8}$$

If the output signals v_{h1} and v_{h2} are connected to a differential amplifier after having ascertained that $I_1 = I_2$, $i'_1 = i'_2$, and $k_1 = k_2$, then the differential output signal

$$v_o = v_{h1} - v_{h2} = i'_1 I_1 k_1 \sin \phi \ . \tag{11.9}$$

The output signal is thus a d.c. voltage, whose response is a function of the peak amplitudes of the input currents and magnetizing currents and of the phase angle between them, as well as of the constant of proportionality k, which depends on the Hall multiplier parameters.

Magnetoresistance bridge circuits in balanced magnetic flux circuits, such as shown in Figures 7.4a and 7.4b can also be used as modulators and demodulators, as shown by Hess [196] and also described by Sun [121]. The magnetic circuit consists of a double loop formed of two E cores, with a magnetizing solenoid wound symmetrically on the two outer legs. The magnetoresistors are mounted in the air gaps of the outer legs. A

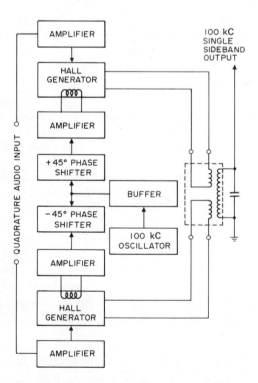

Figure 11.2. Single side-band Hall modulator (after Epstein and Brophy [195]).

permanent magnet is placed in the center leg, and its flux adds every half period to the instantaneous flux of one leg and subtracts from the flux of the other leg. The input signal to the magnetoresistance bridge circuit may be the carrier and the modulation may be impressed on the solenoid. The frequency response of the modulator is determined primarily by core and copper losses; it has no low-frequency cut-off. Alternatively, the carrier may be impressed on the center leg of the magnet, or the carrier and modulation functions may be interchanged and the third variable may be used as a feedback control for the modulation system. Magneto-resistance bridge circuits may also be used as demodulators or detectors. This becomes clear from the following analysis: suppose that two magnetoresistors R_1 and R_2 in a half-bridge circuit are in the air gaps of the outer legs of the two-loop magnetic circuit shown in Figure 7.4. They have instantaneous values of

$$R_1 = R_0(1 + a\sin\omega t)$$

$$R_2 = R_0(1 - a\sin\omega t), \tag{11.10}$$

with R_0 so chosen that $R_1 + R_2 = 2R_0$. Let the potential impressed across the magnetoresistor half-bridge be $V_0 \sin\omega t$, and the d.c. excitation

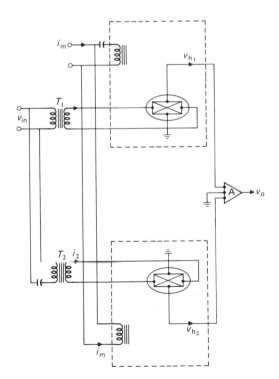

Figure 11.3. Linear phase-sensitive demodulator employing Hall multipliers.

frequency impressed on the solenoid be the same as that of the signal to be demodulated. The current through both magnetoresistors is $i = V_0 \sin \omega t / (R_1 + R_2)$. It may also be expressed as $i = i_0 \sin \omega t$, and the output signal across R_1, $v_o = iR_2$, is

$$v_o = R_0 i_0 (\sin \omega t + a \sin^2 \omega t) . \tag{11.11}$$

The average value of v_o is

$$(v_o)_{av} = \frac{\omega}{2\pi} (R_0 i_0) \int_0^{2\pi/\omega} (\sin \omega t + a \sin^2 \omega t) dt , \tag{11.12}$$

which reduces on integration to

$$(v_o)_{av} = \tfrac{1}{2} R_0 i_0 a , \tag{11.13}$$

and, for the condition $R_1 + R_2 = 2R_0$,

$$(v_o)_{av} = \tfrac{1}{4} a V_0 . \tag{11.14}$$

Thus the average value of the output signal is proportional to the magnetoresistance coefficient a and to the peak value of the input voltage applied to the magnetoresistance half-bridge. It may be increased by a factor of 2 by using a symmetrical full magnetoresistance bridge circuit.

A mixer is a type of modulator in which an input signal of a given frequency interacts with a signal injected by a local oscillator to produce an intermediate frequency (IF) which can then be subjected to further signal processing, for example, in a superheterodyne receiver. In the microwave range suitable mixers are solid-state diodes. They are efficient frequency converters; however, their output signals contain many frequency components, including the sum, difference, and products of the input signal and local oscillator frequencies. The advantage of Hall-effect microwave mixers is that only the sum and difference of the fundamental frequencies are present; their harmonics and higher-order terms are eliminated. Barlow and Krishna [197] have described the design, construction, and performance of Hall plates used as microwave mixers. Two alternative methods are shown in Figure 11.4. In the first, the Hall plate was located in a H_{013} cavity which was resonated at the local oscillator frequency of 9·375 GHz, while current from the input signal of 9·330 GHz was passed through the plate by a wire connected to it. The Hall plate was located at a point of maximum magnetic field and zero electric field, and the Hall output was measured at the difference frequency of 45 MHz. Using an InSb Hall plate, they found that the conversion loss is constant at about 68 dB over a range of signal power from 1 to 20 mW input and 10 W local oscillator power, in agreement with theoretically calculated values. A different mixer configuration, shown in Figure 11.4b, consists of an H_{012} resonant cavity with a Hall plate at its center. The input signal with frequency f_1 provides the E field, which excites a collinear current density vector in the Hall plate.

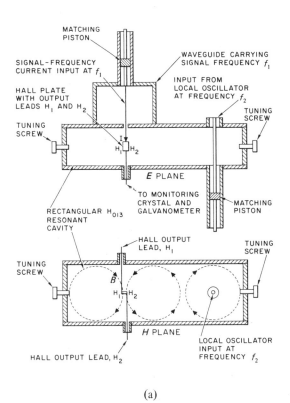

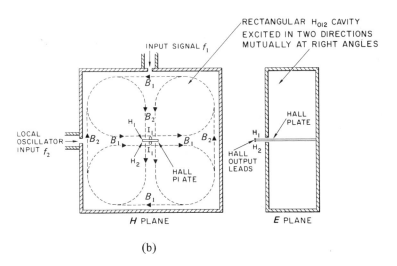

Figure 11.4. Hall effect microwave mixers: (a) H_{013} resonant cavity with input current fed to Hall plate by means of wire leads; (b) H_{012} cavity with input signal induced in Hall plate by tangential magnetic field (after Barlow and Krishna [197]).

The local oscillator (frequency f_2) provides the H field, which is at right angles to the E field, and the resultant Hall voltage is extracted at the difference frequency $f_1 - f_2$. The performance of this mixer is essentially the same as that shown in Figure 11.4a. The conversion losses are still very much higher than those of solid-state diodes. An evaporated film InSb Hall generator, used in conjunction with the arrangement shown in Figure 11.4b, provided a slightly improved efficiency, ~57 dB. However, the film had a high carrier density and low mobility. The potential advantages of better quality films (with mobilities comparable with bulk values) for mixer applications have not been examined as yet. Kataoka and Naito [150] have investigated mixing at 10 GHz in a similar resonant cavity, and obtained comparable results using a two-terminal InSb magnetoresistor in lieu of a Hall plate. Mixing occurs by virtue of the multiplying action inherent in magnetoresistance phenomena.

The potential application of the Hall effect in high-mobility bulk InSb (3 to 5×10^5 cm^2 V^{-1} s^{-1}) at 77°K for frequency conversion in the microwave range was investigated by Chang and Hughes [198] by means of the circuit shown schematically in Figure 11.5. A magnetic field is provided by the input signal with frequency f_1. It interacts in the small InSb Hall specimen with a large electric field supplied by a local oscillator pump source of frequency f_2. The reentrant S-band coaxial cavity is placed within a Dewar held at 77°K. The disc-shaped sample is located on a plane where the radio-frequency magnetic field is high, under the coaxial center post, and the reentrant gap is closed by a high dielectric constant rutile plug. Its purpose is to improve the coupling of the specimen to the radio-frequency field. Both input and pump signals were applied to the coupling loop. The signal provides an azimuthal magnetic field B_ϕ around the sample, and this field modulates the axial field E_z provided by the pump. The resultant Hall field has a radial distribution in the specimen. The cavity had a $Q \approx 60$, and with a pump frequency ~4 MHz greater than the signal frequency the conversion gain of the mixer was determined at 4 MHz. Using a moderate pump power ~0·2 W, the conversion loss was found to be −25 dB and the corresponding bandwidth was ~50 MHz. The conversion loss is due, probably, to inefficient coupling between

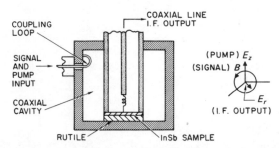

Figure 11.5. Hall effect microwave converter (after Chang and Hughes [198]).

specimen and fields and a less than optimum cavity. The use of Hall multipliers as d.c. to a.c. converters was investigated by Chasmar and Openshaw [199]. Such converters can be used to produce a.c. signals proportional to d.c. input currents or voltages. The a.c. signals can be amplified by means of a stable a.c. amplifier whose rectified output is an amplified replica of the d.c. input signal, without the attendant drift associated with conventional d.c. amplifiers. The optimum circuit configuration is one with the d.c. input signal applied to the Hall generator and with the a.c. modulation applied to the magnetizing solenoid. With a bulk InAs Hall plate a conversion of $0 \cdot 12$ V_{rms} per volt d.c. is obtainable with a carrier breakthrough of ~ 2 μV and a drift of $0 \cdot 3$ μV deg^{-1}. This is comparable with electromechanical, transistor, or electro-optical converters. Hall converters can be driven at higher frequencies, up to several hundred Hz. They offer a further advantage of a low constant input and output impedance throughout the 'chopping' cycle. Similar results were obtained by Weisshaar [200], who obtained a conversion efficiency of $\sim 30\%$ using an InSb Hall generator subjected to an a.c. magnetic field with a peak value of 10 kG. Such Hall converters can be used to produce a modulated alternating voltage output from a variable low-level d.c. signal generated by a thermocouple.

Magnetoresistance-based low-level d.c. to a.c. converters have been investigated analytically and experimentally by Hieronymus and Weiss [201] and by Bechtel et al. [202]. The effective resistance R_B of a magnetoresistor field plate modulated by an a.c. magnetic induction, provided by a simple magnetic circuit and driven by an m.m.f. having an angular frequency ω, can be expressed to a first approximation by

$$R_B = \tfrac{1}{2}(R_P + R_0) + \tfrac{1}{2}(R_P - R_0)\cos 2\omega t , \qquad (11.15)$$

where R_P is the peak resistance induced by the field and R_0 is the zero field resistance. If a d.c. input current i is applied to such a field plate, coupled by means of a capacitor to a load resistance R_L, then the current in the load is

$$i_1 = i\left\{1 - \frac{[\alpha^2(1+\beta)^2 - 1]^{\tfrac{1}{2}}}{\alpha(1+\beta) + \cos^2 \omega t}\right\} , \qquad (11.16)$$

where

$$\alpha = \frac{R_P/R_0 + 1}{R_P/R_0 - 1} \qquad \beta = \frac{2R_L}{R_P + R_0} , \qquad (11.17)$$

as shown by Hieronymus and Weiss [201], who also treated analytically the case of a transformer-coupled load resistance, as well as combinations of reactances and resistance chosen to provide a high conversion efficiency for low-level d.c. input currents in addition to small voltages. Experimentally, they found that the output voltage fluctuations of a magnetoresistance converter with the input leads short-circuited correspond to an input error no greater than $\pm 0 \cdot 03$ μV at $+23°$C over a period of ~ 10 h. Linearity errors are not a significant problem and the troublesome compensation of the misalignment potential, present in Hall converters, is absent in magnetoresistance converters. The potential use of Corbino disc-like magnetoresistor bridge configurations for converting the output of low voltage ($v < 1$ V) and high current ($i > 100$ A) sources, such as solar cells, fuel cells, and thermionic generators from d.c. to a.c. was investigated by Bechtel *et al.* [202]. Transistor bridge circuits used as converters at lower current levels have relatively high internal resistances; InSb or Bi magnetoresistors can be made to have $R_0 \approx 10^{-3}$ Ω. In order to produce a high chopper efficiency, the ratio R_P/R_0 must be made as large as possible without an excessive power expenditure in producing the requisite m.m.f. for the d.c. modulation. Their experimental investigations were made on InSb and Bi Corbino disc magnetoresistor bridge circuits, whose inputs were galvanically coupled to a d.c. source and whose outputs were transformer-coupled to a load resistance. The InSb converters were investigated at $300°$K for an input of 1 A with a magnetic induction of $21 \cdot 5$ kG. The Bi magnetoresistance converters were used at $77°$K with an input of 10 A and a magnetic induction of 20 kG. Using the experimentally determined magnetoresistance parameters, Bechtel *et al.* [202] made a analog computer study of such converters, and reached the conclusion that theoretical conversion efficiencies of 75% are possible provided that electrical and magnetic circuit losses may be considered to be negligible.

A different magnetoresistance d.c. to a.c. converter [203], particularly well suited for InSb + In film magnetoresistors, is shown in Figure 11.6. It is based on the synchronous displacement [3] of a magnetoresistor in the linear gradient of a fixed permanent magnet. The magnetoresistor is translated in the magnetic gradient sinusoidally by a piezoelectric 'bimorph' transducer driven by an audio oscillator, which excites its mechanically resonant frequency. A bimorph consists of bilaminar piezoelectric ceramic strips fixed to an intermediate metallic vane. The piezoelectric laminae have a resonant electric polarization directed along their thicknesses. If electric fields are applied to the strips on each side of the metallic center vane, one expands and the other contracts, owing to their piezoelectric character, thus enhancing the total one-dimensional flexure of the transducer. The a.c. signal developed across the load resistor, R_L is coupled into a narrow-band, tuned audio amplifier by means of capacitive or transformer coupling. The output of the amplifier is fed to a synchronous demodulator. Diodes D_1 and D_2 are maintained in a blocked condition by the $1 \cdot 5$ d.c. bias. The audio oscillator, which drives the piezoelectric bimorph, is also applied to the demodulator through a differentiator and clipper formed by diodes D_3 and D_4 and capacitor C_1. Diodes D_1 and D_2 are unblocked in synchronism with the motion of the

[3] See Equation (10.2) and Figure 10.1, as well as Section 10.1.

magnetoresistor by the differentiated pulses applied to the demodulator bridge circuit. During a portion of this period they can conduct current and deliver to the output terminals, after suitable filtering, a rectified signal which is proportional to the a.c. output derived from the tuned audio amplifier. The main advantage of this synchronous demodulation is the considerable gain in signal to noise, and hence the potential use of the circuit shown in Figure 11.6 for the amplification of low-level d.c. input signals.

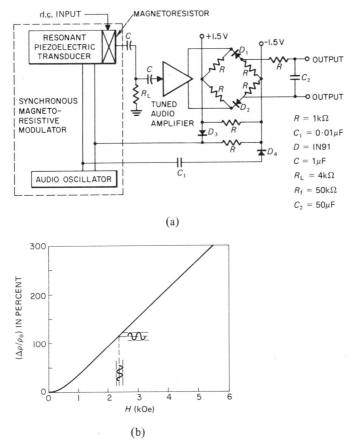

(a)

(b)

Figure 11.6. Magnetoresistive d.c. to a.c. transducer: (a) synchronous modulator with magnetoresistor driven in the air gap of a permanent magnet; (b) transfer characteristic of magnetoresistor showing operating point and modulation produced by displacement in fixed magnetic field gradient.

11.2 Correlators

Hall and magnetoresistor multipliers, by virtue of their flat frequency response which can be made to extend into the video range, are well suited for use in correlators. The general correlation function $\psi_{ab}(\tau)$ of two time-dependent functions $g_a(t)$ and $g_b(t)$ is

$$\psi_{ab}(\tau) = \lim_{T \to \infty} \frac{1}{T} \int_0^T g_a(t)g_b(t-\tau)\,dt \; . \tag{11.18}$$

If the two functions are the same, then $\psi_{ab}(\tau)$ is defined as the auto-correlation function of $g(t)$; if they are different, then Equation (11.18) represents their cross-correlation function. One method of performing correlation measurements is to do it continuously, integrating the product of two functions by means of an integrator with a time constant T_1. The weighted short-term correlation function depends then on τ and on t:

$$\lambda_{ab}(\tau, t) = \frac{1}{T_1} \int_{-\infty}^t g_a(t')g_b(t'-\tau)\exp\left(\frac{t'-t}{\tau}\right)dt' \; . \tag{11.19}$$

An alternative correlation process is to make periodically repeated analyses of samples of finite duration T_2 of the periodic functions $g_a'(t)$ and $g_b'(t)$, and to use an integrator with a time constant T_1. If $T_1 \gg T_2$, then the periodic weighted correlation function, as shown by Billings and Lloyd [204], is

$$\phi_{ab}(\tau_1 T_2) = \frac{\exp(-T_2/T_1)}{T_1[1-\exp(-T_2/T_1)]} \int_0^{T_2} g_a'(t')g_b'(t'-\tau)\exp\left(\frac{t'}{T_1}\right)dt' \; . \tag{11.20}$$

Practical correlators are required to perform three functions: (1) one input signal is to be stored and delayed with respect to the second undelayed signal; (2) the delayed and undelayed signals are multiplied; (3) their product is integrated. Billings and Lloyd [204] have described a low-frequency ($f < 25$ Hz) correlator for the analysis of vocoder control signals. The input signals were applied to Hall modulators, which impressed them on a 2 kHz carrier for recording on standard magnetic tape. One of the tape readout heads was movable, producing the required delay, and the two outputs were applied to a Hall multiplier. The resultant product was applied to a heavily-damped galvanometer, which served in a dual role as integrator and display unit.

Hall multipliers suitable for measuring the autocorrelation function of audio-frequency signals from 15 Hz to 20 kHz were investigated by Holler and Wolf [205] and by Brophy et al. [206], who described the advantages of correlators for improving the sensitivity of low-level amplifiers by two to three orders of magnitude. The cross correlation of two random noise signals is ideally zero. Therefore, if the outputs of two independent amplifier chains are cross-correlated, then their outputs, in the absence of an input signal v_i, presented to both amplifier chains is zero even if the amplifiers have a high internal noise. If these output signals are, respectively,

$$v_a = v_i + v_a'$$
$$v_b = v_i + v_b' \, , \qquad (11.21)$$

then the signal in each channel consists of a correlated component and a statistically-varying component. Their product is

$$v_a v_b = v_i^2 + v_i(v_a' + v_b') + v_a' v_b' \, , \qquad (11.22)$$

and the cross correlation of these time-varying signals is the time average of their product $\langle v_a v_b \rangle = \langle v_i^2 \rangle$; it is this product which is formed by a Hall multiplier with v_a proportional to the input current of the Hall generator, v_b proportional to the magnetic induction, and an RC filter used to produce the time averaging. Brophy *et al.* [206] have shown that a Hall multiplier used in a cross correlator can provide a noise-equivalent input level in audio amplifiers in the range between 5×10^{-15} and 10^{-19} V Hz^{-1}.

A Hall correlator for measuring the autocorrelation and cross-correlation functions of real-time television signals was described by Billings and Forward [207]. In the construction of the multiplier they had to solve two specific problems. The first is a magnetic circuit problem, i.e. keeping the radio-frequency losses of the magnetic core and magnetizing solenoid to a minimum. They solved this problem by using a high-frequency ferrite pot core assembly with a large air gap and only a two-turn solenoid. The second problem concerns the Hall plate. In order to obtain sufficient output power from the Hall plate to drive the integrator, its mobility should be high. However, a high μ_n implies a relatively high conductivity; consequently, the eddy currents induced in the plate by high-frequency magnetic fields can be large. These currents make the establishment of high-frequency magnetic fields more difficult since the Hall plate acts as a short-circuited turn; they also produce a nonuniform field distribution across the plate. The Hall output power is not dependent on the Hall generator thickness, whereas the resistance presented to eddy currents increases as the Hall plate thickness decreases. For this reason Billings and Forward [207] used an evaporated InSb film Hall generator, even though its mobility was much smaller, $\mu_n \approx 10^4$ cm^2 V^{-1} s^{-1}, than that of the bulk material. A video correlator built with such a multiplier was found to have adequate bandwidth for correlation measurements made on high-quality television signals.

11.3 Spectrum analyzers and display systems

Spectrum analyzers are instruments used for determining the frequency components of complex wave forms. The heterodyne wave analyzer is such an instrument. It employs a variable-frequency local oscillator, whose output is multiplied by a complex input signal. This multiplication can be performed by Hall generators or magnetoresistance multipliers. The output of the multiplier is applied to a selective filter, and the local oscillator frequency is adjusted to zero beat with one of the frequency components of the complex input frequency. The variable-frequency local oscillator and the input signal have uncorrelated phases. Consequently heterodyne wave analyzers cannot be used to specify completely the Fourier coefficients of complex periodic signals, since the amplitudes as well as the phase angles of the components need to be known. Periodic electronic signals can be represented as a series of harmonically-related sinusoids:

$$U(\omega t) = a_0 + a_1 \cos \omega t + a_2 \cos 2\omega t + ... + b_1 \sin \omega t + b_2 \sin 2\omega t + ... \ .$$

$$(11.23)$$

The purpose of Fourier signal analysis is the determination of the coefficients a_n and b_n. In practice, Fourier analysis must be performed by numerical or analog procedures, and the series is expressed as

$$U(\omega t) = a_0 + c_1 \cos(\omega t - \theta_1) + ... + c_n \cos(n\omega t - \theta_n),$$

$$c_n = (a_n^2 + b_n^2)^{\frac{1}{2}}, \qquad \theta_n = \tan^{-1}\left(\frac{b_n}{a_n}\right) \ . \qquad (11.24)$$

An apparatus and a technique of Fourier analysis, which yields the magnitudes and the phase angles of the coefficients and does not require a local oscillator, were described by Williams and Denker [208, 209]. Figure 11.7a is a block diagram of such a system. The complex input signal provides the input current to a Hall multiplier and also actuates a pulse generator synchronously. The output pulse is applied to an active tuned circuit, which yields a single-frequency sinusoid harmonically related to the input signal. The output signal of this filter is then applied to a calibrated variable phase shifter, which is adjusted so that the d.c. output of the Hall multiplier reaches a maximum. The value of this d.c. signal is proportional to the magnitude of the specific Fourier coefficient of the complex input signal and the phase shift is related to its phase. This system has two disadvantages: the spectra determined by means of the multiplier output signals are broad and the variable phase shifter is an elaborate and complex item. The system shown in Figure 11.7b overcomes these disadvantages. The complex input signal is again impressed on the Hall multiplier and drives the pulse generator synchronously. Two sinusoidal signals are obtained from the tuned circuit; one has zero phase shift with respect to the input wave, while the other signal is in time-phase quadrature with respect to the input. In order to record the components of the Fourier coefficients from the d.c. output of the Hall multiplier, two readings are required with the multiplier connected alternately to the sine and cosine output terminals of the tuned circuit. The complex periodic input signal, represented as a sum of sinusoidal signals, is applied to the Hall multiplier as the input current of the Hall generator, while the sine wave analyzing signal, a single-frequency sinusoid, generates the transverse magnetic induction. Their product

$$P(\omega t) = \sum_{0,\,p}^{\infty} a_n \cos n\omega t \sin p\omega t + b_n \sin n\omega t \sin p\omega t \ . \tag{11.25}$$

If the complex input signal has a frequency component whose value is identical with the frequency of the analyzing signal, then $P(\omega t)$ has a nonzero average value and the Hall multiplier yields[4] a d.c. output $v_o = \frac{1}{2} b_p$. Williams and Denker [208, 209] have constructed the spectrum analyzer shown in Figure 11.7b. This system was used to analyze distorted nonsymmetrical 100 Hz square waves. Twenty harmonics of such square waves were measured and the results thus obtained compared favorably (~6% discrepancy) with data obtained using a heterodyne spectrum analyzer.

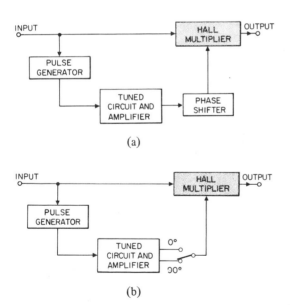

(a)

(b)

Figure 11.7. Spectrum analyzers employing Hall multipliers: (a) complex input signal provides input current to Hall generator and triggers pulse generator synchronously; output signal is Fourier component of input; (b) spectrum analyzer for determining sine and cosine components of distorted nonsymmetrical square waves.

[4] If the analyzing signal is a cosine wave, then the output of the Hall multiplier is $v_o = \frac{1}{2} a_p$.

A magnetic field spectrum analyzer which utilizes the inherently linear
mixing capability of Hall multipliers for the measurement and display of
the frequency components of alternating magnetic fields was described by
Greenstein *et al.* [210]. The instrument was designed to measure magnetic
fields in the frequency range from d.c. to 1 kHz, such as produced by
electrical machines, power lines, and transformers. The input current to
an InSb Hall generator was provided by a fixed-amplitude oscillator whose
frequency was swept linearly from 10 to 11 kHz over a 5 s period. The
Hall generator was mounted between ferrite flux concentrators, whose
parameters were so chosen that the complete spectrum analyzer assembly
was capable of resolving magnetic fields of $\sim 5 \times 10^{-4}$ G to 1 G. The
output of the Hall generator was applied to a narrow-band crystal filter
with a center frequency of 10 kHz and a 10 Hz bandwidth. The output
of the filter was amplified, detected, and applied to the vertical input
plates of a cathode-ray display tube whose horizontal sweep was
synchronized with the oscillator frequency. A sweep rate of 40 Hz s^{-1}
permits the filter response to a single spectral component to build up to
$\sim 70\%$ of its steady-state value and one which gives a 5 s sweep period for
displaying a 200 Hz portion of the spectrum.

Conventional wave analyzers employ heterodyne techniques to produce
an intermediate frequency of ~ 100 kHz, which is then applied to a
narrow-band fixed crystal filter with a 3 to 7 Hz bandwidth. A wave
analyzer for low frequencies, from 20 Hz to 400 Hz, employing Hall
multipliers for heterodyning to d.c. rather than to an intermediate
frequency was described by Anderson and Collins [211]. There are a
number of advantages for employing such a method of wave analysis:
(1) crystal filters can be replaced with simple multisection RC filters;
(2) the frequency stability depends only on the stability of the local
oscillator; (3) to remain within 20% of a 1 Hz passband at 20 Hz, the
local oscillator must vary by no more than $\pm 1\%$ (by $0 \cdot 05\%$ at 400 Hz),
whereas the IF system requires that the local oscillator be stable to
within $\pm 0 \cdot 0002\%$ at 100 kHz. Figure 11.8 is a block diagram of the
main components of such a wave analyzer, whose functions involve taking
the product of the input signal

$$e_{\mathrm{s}} = \sum_{n=1}^{N} E_n \sin(\omega_n t + \theta_n)$$

and of the output of a two-phase oscillator $E_0 \cos \omega_1 t$ and $E_0 \sin \omega_1 t$, and
then filtering out the d.c. components. Suppose that the component of
interest of the input signal is $E_1 \sin(\omega_1 t + \theta_1)$, where θ_1 is the phase
difference between the local oscillator and the input signal. The output
signals of the two RC low-pass filters associated with their respective Hall
multipliers are $\frac{1}{2} E_1 E_0 \sin \theta_1$ and $\frac{1}{2} E_1 E_0 \cos \theta_1$, respectively. These d.c.
voltages represent the magnitude of two vectors displaced from each other
by 90°. The vector-summing circuit shown in Figure 11.8 converts the

d.c. signals into a.c. voltages phase-shifted by 90° from each other. The vector sum of the a.c. voltages appears at the output of the operational amplifier. It is proportional to the amplitude of the selected frequency component of the input signal. A wave analyzer of this type [211] was found to behave as a very stable narrow-band filter. Its dynamic range, bounded primarily by the Hall multiplier, was linear within ±0·5 dB over

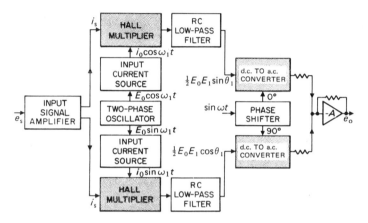

Figure 11.8. Audio-frequency wave analyzer using Hall multipliers for heterodyning to d.c., instead of an intermediate frequency.

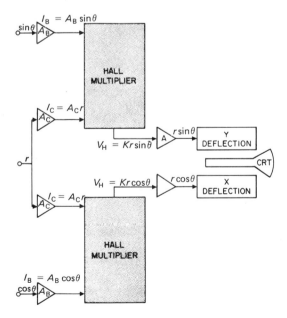

Figure 11.9. Polar coordinate display of two input variables; Hall multipliers are used to transform polar to rectangular coordinates (after Smerage [212]).

a dynamic range of 60 dB and the −3 dB bandwidth; the measured frequency response of the filter was 4·4 Hz. Particular care is required, however, in stabilizing and eliminating harmonics from the local oscillator.

Polar displays of two variables can be represented on a cathode-ray tube by using Hall multipliers to produce a transformation of coordinates, as shown by Smerage [212]. Figure 11.9 is a block diagram of such a polar display system. It can be used to represent the signal vector of direction-finding apparatus, sonar systems, or as a plan-position indicator for radar. The input signals to the apparatus are chosen to be proportional to the strength r of a signal arriving at the azimuthal angle θ. The functions $\sin\theta$ and $\cos\theta$ may be generated electronically, or they may be produced by resolvers or synchros attached to a directional antenna adjusted to receive the signal r. Hall multipliers are used to multiply r by $\cos\theta$ and by $\sin\theta$, respectively, and thus to produce the required transformation to rectangular coordinates, $x = r\cos\theta$ and $y = r\sin\theta$. The output signals x and y are then applied to a cathode-ray tube with magnetic or electrostatic xy deflection, and the pattern displayed on its screen is a polar representation of the vector $\bar{r}$. For Hall generators with a 1% linearity, Smerage [212] found the radial accuracy to be better than ±2% of the radius vector and the angular accuracy to be better than ±2·5° from 0° to 360°.

11.4 Magnetic recording playback transducers

Magnetic recording [213] and playback involves the storage of a multipolar remanent magnetization of variable magnetic intensity on a ferromagnetic storage medium, such as a magnetic tape, drum, or disc. The conventional method of magnetic recording includes a 'write' or recording process and a 'read' or playback procedure. In the write process a small region of the recording medium is subjected to a magnetic field equal to or greater than its coercive force, so that a remanent magnetic flux Φ_r is present in that region after the magnetic field is removed. The write field is produced by a write 'head', which usually consists of a solenoid wound on a high-permeability core having a narrow air gap. The write field acts in and around this gap, in close proximity to the recording medium, and its parameters define the size of the recorded region. In the playback process the remanent flux or its time derivative is converted into a corresponding voltage by a playback transducer. A conventional inductive playback transducer [214] is similar to the write head, its solenoid having N turns links a fraction m of the recorded flux Φ_r. The voltage v_L induced in the solenoid is

$$v_L = mN \frac{d\Phi_r}{dt} .$$

$$(11.26)$$

The fractional flux acting on the transducer is a function of many variables, which include, for example, the permeability of the transducer core, the orientation of the magnetization vector in the recording medium, the thickness of the latter, and the spacing between the recorded flux source and the playback transducer.   A simple inductive playback transducer consists of a high-permeability ring, having a gap of length δ and of width s in contact with the recording medium.   The latter is considered to have a displacement velocity v.   If a sinusoidal signal with frequency f is recorded upon it, then the recorded wavelength $\lambda_r = v/f$ and the output signal in the inductive playback transducer is

$$v_L \propto F\frac{\delta}{\lambda_r} fs\Phi_r \ , \tag{11.27}$$

where $F(\delta/\lambda_r)$ is a function which depends on the parameters δ, v, and f. Equation (11.27) states that v_L is a function of the frequency of the recorded signal.   At low frequencies v_L decreases monotonically, as shown in Figure 11.10.   Low-frequency response is required of magnetic playback transducers if data recorded, for example, on magnetic tape at conventional velocities used for tape recording are to be played back slowly for analysis and evaluation [215], or if control and reference signals are recorded and must be detected at varying rates, or if the tape is to be moved incrementally or discontinuously.   Amplifiers used in conjunction with inductive playback transducers require a considerable boost in their low-frequency response in order to equalize the overall frequency response of high fidelity tape-recording systems.   Furthermore, an increase in storage density of recorded information by means of parallel recording tracks and a corresponding number of inductive playback transducers is limited by the dependence of v_L on s.   The width of a transducer cannot be decreased without decreasing v_L; such a decrease would be desirable in order to stack a number of them side by side for parallel readout.   An increase in longitudinal storage density by decreasing the velocity v of the recording medium, and also by decreasing δ, is feasible only over a

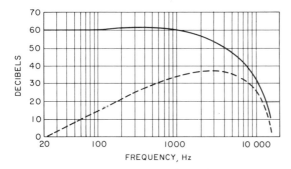

Figure 11.10. Unequalized frequency dependence of magnetic recording playback transducers; dashed curve represents response of conventional transducer responding to rate of change of magnetic flux; solid curve represents response of flux-sensitive transducer (after Camras [218]).

relatively narrow range of v because of the attendant decrease of v_L with v. Furthermore, if the gap reluctance is smaller than that of the magnetic circuit, then the flux acting on the solenoid winding of the transducer decreases sharply.

A number of techniques for improving the response of inductive playback transducers have been suggested and put to use. One of the most successful of these is a magnetic modulator [216]. The recorded flux element modulates a high-frequency biasing magnetic induction, produced by a solenoid wound on a saturable portion of the same ferromagnetic core of the transducer as the output winding. The latter detects the second harmonic of the biasing signal frequency. The output impedances of inductive and modulator playback transducers are reactive, and owing to domain wall motion in the ferromagnetic core, the resultant Barkhausen noise sets a lower limit on the detectable flux amplitudes. The main advantage of such transducers is that they sense the recorded magnetic induction rather than its time derivative. The same function can also be performed by Hall-effect playback transducers acting, in effect, as low-level magnetometers [217, 218].

In principle, Hall generators can be used directly without attendant magnetic circuits, and advantage may be taken of their extended frequency response for detecting wide-band high-frequency recorded signals. However, the incremental magnetic sensitivity of most Hall generators is too low to detect the slight values of Φ_r, and in order to increase it they are mounted either in the front gap or in the rear gap of a magnetic circuit [219–221], such as shown in Figure 11.11. The magnetic core elements act as flux concentrators for Φ_r. Nonlinear ferromagnetic phenomena associated with magnetic hysteresis and domain wall motion, such as present in modulator transducers, are absent. Table 11.1 compares some of the relevant properties of the two types of playback transducers.

The magnetic induction B acting on a Hall transducer such as shown in Figure 11.11a can be defined in terms of the approximate expression

$$B \approx \Phi_r \left(\frac{w_c/w}{1 + S(d/G)w_c/w} \right) , \tag{11.28}$$

where w_c is the width of the core (equal to the track width), w is the width, and l the length of the Hall generator and that of the corresponding adjacent portions of the core shown in Figure 11.11a. G is the length of the front gap and S is its width. The saturated magnetic flux density of typical magnetic tape is $\sim 0 \cdot 8$ maxwell cm^{-1}. However, m is typically of the order of $0 \cdot 1$; the flux levels do not introduce any magnetoresistance effects. The thickness d of a Hall generator is significant, not only because v_h increases with decreasing d, but also because of the effect of a decrease in d on the reluctance of the rear air gap.

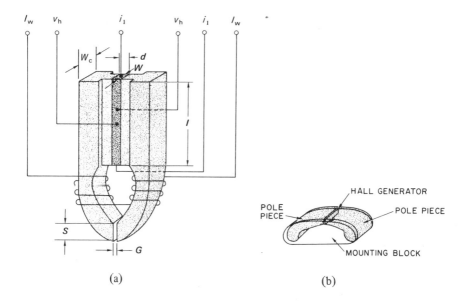

Figure 11.11. Hall playback transducers: (a) Hall generator placed in rear air gap between ferromagnetic cores; solenoid winding and current I_w can be used to 'write' information on magnetic recording medium; (b) Hall generator mounted in front air gap between ferrite pole pieces of magnetic circuit.

Table 11.1. A comparison of typical Hall and magnetic modulator playback transducers.

Parameter	Modulator transducer	Hall playback transducer
Input current	a.c. only 100 mA, 7·5 kHz	d.c., a.c., or pulse 25 mA
Source impedance	37 mH	25 ohm
Load impedance	0·25 mH	50 ohm
Temperature stability	$10 \ \mu V \ deg^{-1}$	$22 \ \mu V \ deg^{-1}$
Open-circuit output	12 mV	5 mV
Noise output	Barkhausen noise ~50 dB below saturation output level	thermal noise in bulk, $1/f$ noise in films
Output signal	a.c., 15 kHz	a.c., d.c., or pulse
Track width	~0·08 cm	~0·15 cm

The ratio of recorded signal to noise is independent of the displacement velocity of the recording medium, because the amplitudes of both signal and noise vary in the same way with v. However, the noise in follow-up amplifiers connected to such a transducer is considerably greater than the recorded noise, and consequently the signal and noise are uncorrelated. Hall playback transducers, on the other hand, have a response [222] which does not depend on the frequency of the recorded signal or the velocity of displacement of the medium. The signal-to-noise ratio is not dependent on v and, because the density of longitudinally-recorded information and the resolution is limited by the minimum tolerable signal-to-noise ratio at the low end of the recorded spectrum, Hall transducers offer advantages [223, 224] in this respect owing to their flat frequency response shown in Figure 11.10. The Hall output voltage is independent of v, so that recorded signals can be reproduced from a discontinuously or incrementally displaced recording medium. The state of magnetization can also be determined with the recording medium in a stationary state, as described in Chapter 6 and Figure 6.10. A further advantage of Hall playback transducers is their resistive output impedance, which is more compatible with follow-up transistor amplifiers than the reactive impedance of inductive and modulator-type transducers. A disadvantage of playback transducers, which sense Φ_r rather than its time derivative, is the requirement of shielding the transducer from stray magnetic fields and compensating for the Earth's magnetic field. In the case of Hall transducers the problems associated with drift, thermal effects, and misalignment potential must, of course, be surmounted as well.

11.5 Nonreciprocal devices
A two-port network characterized by the matrix

$$\begin{vmatrix} r_{11} & r_{12} \\ r_{21} & r_{22} \end{vmatrix} \tag{11.29}$$

is reciprocal if it is symmetric about a main diagonal, $r_{12} = r_{21}$. Networks which do not satisfy this reciprocity criterion are called 'nonreciprocal'. McMillan [239] described mechanical nonreciprocal systems and subsequently [240] suggested the Hall effect as a phenomenon for achieving nonreciprocity in electrodynamics. Tellegen [241] introduced the term 'gyrator' for a passive nonreciprocal network element, in addition to the other passive reciprocal network elements, such as resistors, capacitors, inductors, and transformers. An ideal gyrator is a four-pole, defined by the set of equations such as

$$v_1 = -ri_2$$
$$v_2 = ri_1 . \tag{11.30}$$

It resembles the ideal transformer[5], except for the change in sign and the fact that it 'gyrates' current into voltage and *vice versa*. A Hall generator may be considered as a passive, linear, nonreciprocal network. Suppose that an inductance is connected across its Hall electrodes[6]. Then, in terms of Equation (4.1), the potential developed across this reactance is $-j\omega L i_2$. The corresponding four-pole equations are

$$v_1 = R_{11} i_1 + R_{12} i_2$$
$$i_2 (j\omega L + R_{22}) = R_{12} i_1 \ . \tag{11.31}$$

The Hall generator acts as an impedance inverter [242, 243]; the input impedance has a capacitive component $-j(R_{12}^2/\omega L)$:

$$\frac{v_1}{i_1} = R_{11} + \frac{R_{12}^2}{R_{22} + j\omega L} \approx R_{11} - j\frac{R_{12}^2}{\omega L} \ . \tag{11.32}$$

A Hall-effect gyrator operates at d.c. and, theoretically, at any frequency up to the dielectric relaxation time of the material used. Mason *et al.* [246] gave an analytic description of Hall gyrators, including magnetoresistance effects, and also made experimental investigations on Ge gyrators. Wick [247] published a detailed analysis of Hall gyrators, in which he considered the location and size of their electrodes and their effect on the performance of such devices. He concluded that the minimum insertion loss of a four-pole gyrator is $7 \cdot 66$ dB. Arlt [254] considered the use of multiterminal gyrators for improving their efficiency. Using InSb rhombic-shaped plates with a number of input and output circuits, he obtained efficiencies up to 50%.

The maximum efficiency of a four-pole gyrator expressed [244] in terms of the ratio of the maximum Hall output power to input power is

$$\eta_{max} = \frac{(k^2 + 1)^{\frac{1}{2}} - 1}{(k^2 + 1)^{\frac{1}{2}} + 1} \text{ with } k^2 = \frac{R_{12} R_{21}}{R_{11} R_{22}} \ . \tag{11.33}$$

For $B \rightarrow \infty$, the parameter k tends towards unity and consequently towards $\eta_{max} = 0 \cdot 172$. It may also be expressed in terms of the Hall tangent, $\tan\phi = \mu B$, as shown by Renton [245]:

$$\eta_{max} = \frac{[(\mu B)^2 + 1]^{\frac{1}{2}} - 1}{[(\mu B)^2 + 1]^{\frac{1}{2}} + 1} = \frac{1 - \cos\phi}{1 + \cos\phi} \ . \tag{11.34}$$

Gruetzmann [244] has shown that considerably higher efficiencies may be obtained from Hall gyrators with more than four terminals. The maximum efficiency of a gyrator with an infinite number of terminals tends towards

[5] An ideal transformer can be regarded as two gyrators connected in series, and a capacitor as a gyrator terminated in an inductance.

[6] Magnetically-tunable solid-state inductors (up to several hundred μH) based on the nonreciprocal properties of capacitively-loaded InSb Hall generators were described by Kataoka *et al.* [264].

unity in terms of Equation (11.34). For n input terminals and m output terminals, the parameter k in Equation (11.33) is to be expressed as $k^2 = nm$. For a given Hall angle ϕ, the maximum efficiency of a Hall generator with an arbitrary number of electrodes is then between the limits determined [245] from Equations (11.33) and (11.34). Experimental verification was obtained on polycrystalline and single-crystal InSb plates, 10 to 50 μm thick ($\mu B = 10$ at room temperature), with 12 circuits per side, held in a constant magnetic induction of 18·5 kG. The efficiency of the gyrator was found to be $\eta_{max} = 0·605$.

An isolator is a two-port device, which allows the propagation of electromagnetic energy in one direction and inhibits its propagation in the opposite direction. It is characterized by the presence of a zero in one of the off-diagonal elements of a 2 × 2 impedance matrix.

A Hall isolator, such as shown in Figure 11.12a, also called a skew gyrator [248], consists of a four-terminal Hall plate with asymmetrically-disposed electrodes[7]. The transfer resistance between its two ports consists of an ohmic component, in addition to the nonreciprocal magnetic field-dependent component:

$$R_{12} = R - R_{12}(B)$$

$$R_{21} = R + R_{21}(B) .$$ (11.35)

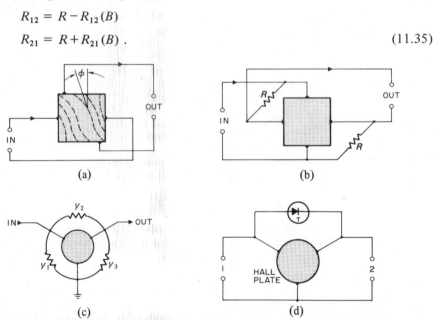

(a)

(b)

(c)

(d)

Figure 11.12. Nonreciprocal devices based on Hall effect: (a) skew gyrator with asymmetrically-disposed electrodes; (b) Hall isolator; (c) unidirectional negative resistance amplifier; (d) three-terminal Hall isolator and tunnel diode amplifier.

[7] Two Hall gyrators of the same geometrical configuration with peripheral electrodes, whose extent, on one specimen, is the reciprocal ratio of the extent on the other specimen, have the same nonreciprocity, voltage transfer ratio, and the same maximum efficiency (Haeusler, J., 1965, *Arch. Elektrische Ubertr.*, **20**, 201).

If R is so chosen that, for a given transverse magnetic induction B, $R = R_{12}(B)$, then the conditions required of an isolator are met; $R_{12} = 0$ and R_{21} has twice the value of the symmetric Hall plate configuration:

$$v_1 = i_1 R_{11}$$
$$v_2 = 2i_1 R + i_2 R_{22} \ . \tag{11.36}$$

A skew gyrator is dependent on variations in charge-carrier mobility, temperature, and magnetic induction because of the dependence of the Hall angle upon these parameters. Its efficiency is

$$\eta = \left(\frac{R_{21}}{2R_{11}} \right)^2 \ . \tag{11.37}$$

An isolator may also be built [246] using a four-terminal Hall plate with symmetrically-disposed electrodes, such as shown in Figure 11.12b, provided that its input and output terminals are loaded by a linear resistor R, so chosen that

$$R = \frac{(R_{11}^2 + R_{21}^2)^2}{2R_{21}} \ . \tag{11.38}$$

The efficiency of such an isolator, in the forward direction, is

$$\eta = \frac{(R_{21}/R_{11})^2}{(1 + R_{21}/R_{11})^2} \ . \tag{11.39}$$

The properties of transformer-coupled four-pole skew gyrators, made, respectively, of 10 μm and 80 μm thick InSb plates with $\mu_n = 5 \times 10^4$ cm^2 V^{-1} s^{-1}, were investigated experimentally at room temperature by Kobus [249]. He determined the coefficient of isolation α, a figure of merit of an isolator, in terms of the forward to reverse power transfer ratio as a function of frequency. He found that α decreases monotonically with frequency from about 50 dB at 10 MHz to about 24 dB at 240 MHz, for the 10 μm thick plate. The 80 μm thick plate had a poorer frequency response: $\alpha \approx 24$ dB at ~50 MHz. The reason appears to be the higher internal resistance of the thinner plate, which reduces the significance of inductive coupling, the primary cause of the limited frequency response. The experimental data were best represented by an equivalent circuit consisting of an ideal isolator, the input and output circuits of which were coupled by a transformer, whose mutual inductance and input and output impedances were determined by the physical size and position of the isolator and its leads. The efficiency of isolators can be increased by using a Hall plate with multiple input and output electrodes, as shown by Gruetzmann [244]. Using an intrinsic InSb gyrator with nine pairs of input and output circuits and a resistive termination of 91 Ω, he obtained an efficiency $\eta = 0 \cdot 717$ in the forward direction and $\eta \approx 10^{-5}$ in the reverse direction. The reverse attenuation was typically 85 dB at $0 \cdot 1$ MHz and 70 dB at 1 MHz, dropping off below 10 MHz.

Hall isolators may be combined with tunnel diodes or other negative resistance devices [250, 251] to produce a unidirectional amplifier. Such an amplifier gives a finite gain for the forward direction of signal propagation and (ideally) an infinite attenuation for the reverse direction. A simple negative resistance amplifier is shown schematically in Figure 11.12c. If the negative parallel conductances y_1, y_2, y_3 are not connected and a transverse magnetic induction is applied to the gyrator, then the short-circuit admittances are

$$y_{11} = \left(\frac{i_1}{v_1}\right)_{v_2 = 0} \qquad y_{22} = \left(\frac{i_2}{v_2}\right)_{v_1 = 0} = y_0$$

$$y_{12} = \left(\frac{i_1}{v_2}\right)_{v_1 = 0} \qquad y_{21} = \left(\frac{i_2}{v_1}\right)_{v_2 = 0} . \qquad (11.40)$$

Suppose that a parameter α, which is an odd function of the Hall angle ϕ, is chosen so that $|\alpha| < 1$ and

$$y_{12} = -\tfrac{1}{2}y_0(1-\alpha) , \qquad y_{21} = -\tfrac{1}{2}y_0(1+\alpha) . \qquad (11.41)$$

If the negative conductances are now connected to the circuit and are given the values $y_1 = y_3 = y_{21}$ and $y_2 = y_{12}$, then it can be shown [246, 251] that $i_1 = 0$ and $i_2 = \alpha v_0 v_1$. The device can be made to behave as an isolator, with gain in the forward signal propagation direction.

A detailed analysis of Hall isolators used in conjunction with tunnel diodes was made by Kroemer [252]. He showed that the impedance of Hall isolators can be made to match that of tunnel diodes, producing a large unidirectional gain compared with the insertion loss of the isolator. If the tunnel diode is in shunt with the input terminals of a four-pole isolator, then the resultant unidirectional amplifier has no voltage gain, a high current, and a high power gain when the tunnel diode negative resistance $-R$ approaches that of R_{11}; the input resistance of the isolator stabilizes the operating (quiescent) point of the tunnel diode. If the tunnel diode shunts the output of the isolator, then the output impedance becomes very high if R_{22} approaches the value of $-R$; the amplifier has no current gain, a high voltage gain, and very high power gain. On the other hand, if the tunnel diode is in series with the isolator input, then, provided that $-R \approx R_{11}$, the voltage gain of the amplifier is high, but both the input and output impedances are low, particularly the input impedance, which approaches a zero value. A disadvantage of such an amplifier is its instability. Its operating point is a function of the input signal source impedance. The same is true of a circuit in which the tunnel diode is in series with the output terminals of the isolator. Such an amplifier has a moderate input impedance, a near-zero output impedance, and a high current gain. The frequency response of the series-type amplifiers is poorer than that of the parallel-type amplifiers.

Grubbs [251] has shown that a unidirectional amplifier, with one tunnel diode in shunt with the input of a four-terminal isolator, matched so that $-R_1 \approx R_{11}$, and another tunnel diode in shunt with its output $-R_2 \approx R_{22}$, can provide considerable advantages over the above-described devices. Such an amplifier has the high input impedance and the high current gain of the shunted input device and the high output impedance and high voltage gain of the shunted output device. The voltage gain bandwidth product of such an amplifier is $g_T/4\pi RC$, where g_T, determined by the isolator, has values typically between $0 \cdot 1$ and 1 and RC is the time constant of the tunnel diode.

Experimental investigations of isolators connected to tunnel diode amplifiers were also made by Hubbard et al. [253]. They encountered difficulties in suppressing spurious oscillations of the tunnel diodes due to stray inductances and coupling leads. To overcome these problems, they used a three-terminal Hall isolator such as shown in Figure 11.12d, whose impedance matrix can be written in the form

$$
\begin{vmatrix}
R_c & R_c(\tfrac{1}{2}+\alpha) \\
R_c(\tfrac{1}{2}-\alpha) & R_c
\end{vmatrix}
\tag{11.42}
$$

where R_c is the resistance between any two terminals and α, a measure of the nonreciprocity, is a function only of the Hall angle. For each value of R_c and α there are two possible values of the tunnel diode negative resistance which produce perfect isolation:

$$
R_N = \frac{R_c(\tfrac{3}{4}+\alpha^2)}{\tfrac{1}{2} \pm \alpha} \ .
\tag{11.43}
$$

The plus sign in Equation (11.43) provides isolation in the $2 \to 1$ direction. The gain $G_{1 \to 2}$ in the $1 \to 2$ direction is given by

$$
G_{1 \to 2} = \left(\frac{\alpha}{\tfrac{1}{2}-\alpha}\right)^2 \ .
\tag{11.44}
$$

For values of α greater than $\tfrac{1}{4}$, the transmission in the $1 \to 2$ direction is greater than unity, resulting in power gain. The values of R_N are greater than R_c, and thus satisfy the d.c. stability criterion of the tunnel diode. Hubbard et al. [253] obtained gain–bandwidth products of 200 to 300 MHz using a three-terminal InSb Hall isolator in a field, $B = 4 \cdot 2$ kG, and a 1N2941 tunnel diode.

A circulator [248] is an n-port device ($n > 2$), in which a signal applied to one port is transmitted only to one adjacent port. Figure 11.13a shows a three-port Hall circulator, which consists of a circular semiconductor plate with six equispaced ohmic contacts and with a transverse magnetic induction normal to its surface plane. Other geometrical configurations, such as polygons, may be chosen for the Hall plate [255]. If the proper value of B acts upon the circulator plate

shown in Figure 11.13a, then no output appears across the terminals
3,3'—only across the terminals 2,2'. The sequence of forward
transmission is $1 \to 2 \to 3 \to 1$. If a load is attached to the terminals so
that a current can flow through them, then the Hall angle is decreased.
A larger value of B is then required for rebalancing the circulator. Let
the short-circuit shunt admittances of such a circulator be defined as
$y_{mm} = i_m/v_n$, with all v's $= 0$ except v_n. The set of three equations
relating the voltages, currents, and admittances are [256]

$$i_m = \sum_{n=1}^{3} y_{mn} v_n , \qquad m = 1, 2, 3 . \tag{11.45}$$

If the circulator is symmetrical, then the admittances can be expressed as

$$y_{11} = y_{22} = y_{33} = y_S$$

$$y_{13} = y_{21} = y_{32} = y_F$$

$$y_{12} = y_{23} = y_{31} = y_R . \tag{11.46}$$

The equivalent circuit of the symmetrical circulator is shown in
Figure 11.13b. Let the admittance of loads applied across the ports of
the device be y_L; the input admittance y_{in} is then

$$y_{in} = y_S \left[1 + \frac{U_F^3 + U_R^3 - 2U_R U_F(1 + U_L)}{(1 + U_L)^2 - U_R U_F} \right] , \tag{11.47}$$

where the normalized admittances are $U_F = y_F/y_S$, $U_R = y_R/y_S$, and
$U_L = y_L/y_S$. The forward voltage transmission ratio is

$$\frac{v_F}{v_{in}} = \frac{U_R^2 - U_F(1 + U_L)}{(1 + U_L)^2 - U_R U_F} , \tag{11.48}$$

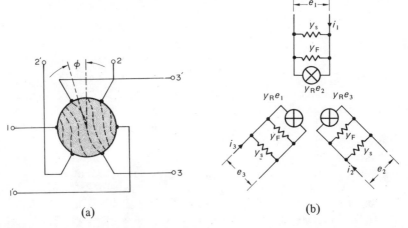

(a)   (b)

Figure 11.13. Three-port Hall circulator: (a) schematic circuit configuration;
(b) equivalent circuit (after Grubbs [256]).

and the reverse transmission ratio is

$$\frac{v_R}{v_{in}} = \frac{U_F^2 - U_R(1 + U_L)}{(1 + U_L)^2 - U_R U_F} \ . \tag{11.49}$$

In order that the circuit have the properties of a circulator, the reverse voltage transmission ratio must be zero; the load admittance calculated from Equation (11.49) is, therefore,

$$y_L = \frac{y_F^2}{y_R} - y_S \ . \tag{11.50}$$

Three-port Hall circulators with a forward attenuation of 17 dB and a reverse attenuation of 61 dB were described by Grubbs [256]. In a magnetic induction $B = 0 \cdot 65$ kG, the efficiency $\eta \approx 0 \cdot 015$, and, for a properly loaded circulator and $B = 15$ kG, the efficiency $\eta = 0 \cdot 056$. However, if more than one pair of terminals are used for each input port, a considerable increase can be obtained in the efficiency of a circulator, as shown by Gruetzmann [244]. For five pairs of control and load circuits in 10 kG (using intrinsic InSb), he obtained an efficiency $\eta \approx 0 \cdot 4$ and, for a circulator with ten control and load circuits in $B = 18$ kG, $\eta_{max} = 0 \cdot 605$ in the frequency range of $9 \cdot 5$ kHz to $2 \cdot 1$ MHz.

Special-purpose circuits and devices

Hall generators and magnetoresistors described in the preceding chapters are discrete devices rather than portions of functionally integrated circuits used in transducers. The homogeneous semiconductors or two-phase pseudobinary alloys employed for their construction are free of p–n junctions and phenomena associated with minority carriers are considered to play a negligible role in their operation and use. Their electrodes are considered to be noninjecting and to have an ohmic character. These restrictions are lifted for the devices and applications described in the following sections. Magnetic transducers employing diodes and transistors in conjunction with active integrated circuits, for amplification of the signals derived across magnetic field-sensitive elements, are of current topical interest and are described in Sections 12.1 and 12.2. Section 12.3 deals with the nonreciprocal properties inherent in the Hall effect and its circuit applications for the construction of gyrators, isolators, and circulators.

12.1 Junction Hall generators

In an intrinsic semiconductor subjected to transverse electric and magnetic fields, electrons as well as holes are deflected in the same direction, because $\pm e$ corresponds to $\pm v$, and consequently the Lorentz force $F = evB$ is invariant with the sign of the charge carriers. In materials or structures in which electrons are the majority carriers, the hole concentration in the vicinity of the boundary to which they are deflected by the combined action of the electric and magnetic fields increases until the hole excess is limited by bulk and surface electron–hole recombination processes. This is defined as the Suhl–Shockley [225] effect, and Hall generator junction devices described subsequently are based upon it.

Figure 12.1a shows schematically a junction Hall generator configuration. It has ohmic contacts at both ends of the rectangular bar and a reverse-biased rectifying junction at its midpoint. A magnetic field applied normal to the plane of the page produces a hole gradient along the x direction. The holes diffusing into the reverse-biased junction cause an increase in the reverse current, which is a nonlinear function of the magnetic field. If the reverse impedance of the junction is high, then R may be of the order of 10^5 Ω, and consequently reverse current changes of a few tens of μA can produce changes of several volts across the load resistance R, in accordance with Figure 12.1b. The output signal at zero current may be eliminated by a two-junction configuration with a balanced output circuit, such as shown in Figure 12.2. The output signal has a polarity which depends on the direction of the signal current and the sense of the applied magnetic field. A first-order one-dimensional theoretical evaluation of such devices and a comparison with the performance of germanium junction Hall generators was given by Milnes and Weber [226].

The assumptions used in the analysis included the following conditions: (1) the electron density (in n-type material) remains considerably greater than the hole density so that conductivity modulation is negligible; (2) the junction depletion layer thickness is negligible with respect to the width of the rectangular bar shown in Figure 12.1a; (3) the decay of excess holes is considered to be represented by a bulk lifetime τ_B

$$\frac{dp}{dt} = \frac{1}{\tau_B}(p - p_0) \, . \tag{12.1}$$

The electron lifetime is considered to be identically τ_B and the surface recombination velocity, where considered, is represented by s cm s^{-1}.

Let the flow of electrons in the x direction of Figure 12.1a be N per unit area per second at a point x from the left-hand face of the device.

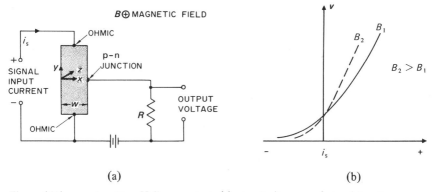

(a)   (b)

Figure 12.1. p–n junction Hall generator: (a) circuit diagram of signal input, source, and output voltage of single-junction transducer; (b) output voltage as a function of input current with magnetic induction as a parameter.

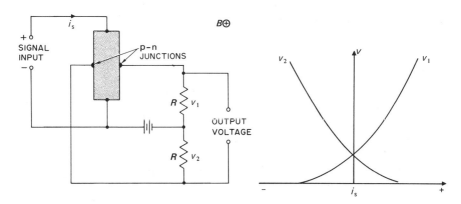

Figure 12.2. Double-junction Hall transducer with balanced output circuit (after Milnes and Weber [226]).

The signal current i_s produces an electric field E_y (independent of x) and the electron velocity in the y direction $v_y = \mu_n E_y$. The Lorentz force in the x direction $F = -e\mu_n E_y B$, and this is opposed by an electric field force $-eE_x$. Including one-dimensional diffusion,

$$N = \mu_n n(\mu_n E_y B - E_x) - D_n \frac{dn}{dx} \tag{12.2}$$

where D_n is the diffusion coefficient and n the volume density of electrons. From the continuity of electron flow, $\partial N/\partial t = -\partial n/\partial t$, and, by introducing an equation such as Equation (12.1) into Equation (12.2) to account for the balance of recombination and generation of electrons,

$$\frac{\partial n}{\partial t} = D_n \frac{\partial^2 n}{\partial x^2} - \frac{\partial}{\partial x} [n(\mu_n^2 E_y B - \mu_n E_x)] - \frac{n - n_0}{\tau_B} . \tag{12.3}$$

In the steady state $dn/dt = 0$; therefore

$$D_n \frac{d^2 n}{dx^2} - (\mu_n^2 E_y B - \mu_n E_x) \frac{dn}{dx} + n\mu_n \frac{dE_x}{dx} - \frac{n - n_0}{\tau_B} = 0 . \tag{12.4}$$

A similar derivation is applicable for the holes and leads to

$$D_p \frac{d^2 p}{dx^2} - (\mu_p^2 E_y B + \mu_p E_x) \frac{dp}{dx} - p\mu_p \frac{dE_x}{dx} - \frac{p - p_0}{\tau_B} = 0 . \tag{12.5}$$

If charge neutrality is presumed to be present in the bulk, then the field strength $E_x = \mu_n E_y B$ is a constant and consequently $dE_x/dx = 0$. Equation (12.5) can be expressed as

$$D_p \frac{d^2 p}{dx^2} - (\mu_p^2 E_y B + \mu_p \mu_n E_y B) \frac{dp}{dx} - \frac{p - p_0}{\tau_B} = 0 . \tag{12.6}$$

Let the diffusion length be expressed as $L_p = (D_p \tau_B)^{\frac{1}{2}}$ and the effective hole density as $p' = p - p_0$. Then Equation (12.6) becomes, in terms of these parameters,

$$\frac{d^2 p'}{dx^2} - A \frac{dp'}{dx} - \frac{p'}{L_p^2} = 0 , \tag{12.7}$$

where the coefficient A is a function of the magnetic induction and of the scattering parameter r, which has a value of $3\pi/8$ for acoustic scattering and unity for polar or neutral impurity scattering:

$$A = r \frac{\mu_p B E_y}{D_p} (\mu_n + \mu_p) . \tag{12.8}$$

Equation (12.7) admits a standard solution of the form

$$p' = a_1 \exp m_1 x + a_2 \exp m_2 x$$
$$m_1 = \tfrac{1}{2} A + [(\tfrac{1}{2} A)^2 + (L_p)^{-2}]^{\frac{1}{2}}$$
$$m_2 = \tfrac{1}{2} A - [(\tfrac{1}{2} A)^2 + (L_p)^{-2}]^{\frac{1}{2}} , \tag{12.9}$$

and subject to the boundary conditions, in the absence of surface
generation–recombination phenomena, of the form

$$p\mu_p(\mu_p E_y B + E_x) = D_p \frac{dp}{dx} \tag{12.10}$$

at $x = 0$, where the drift current and the diffusion current of holes balance
each other. At the junction, $x = w$, $p = 0$ and, because the junction is
reverse-biased, the current density

$$J_p(w) = -eD_p \frac{dp}{dx} . \tag{12.11}$$

The differential term in Equation (12.11) is obtained by differentiating
p' with respect to x after the appropriate boundary conditions are
introduced into Equation (12.9). In the presence of surface recombination
the hole concentration at the junction [Equaton (12.9)] must be solved
in terms of the boundary condition

$$-sp' = p\mu_p(\mu_p BE_y - E_x) - D_p \frac{dp}{dx} \tag{12.12}$$

instead of Equation (12.10). Milnes and Weber have solved for the current
density $J_p(w)$ as a function of the parameter $\frac{1}{2}A$, taking $L_p = 0\cdot081$ cm
and $w = 0\cdot25$ cm. Figure 12.3a shows the normalized current densities
$J_p/J_p(A = 0)$ as a function of $\frac{1}{2}A$, with s/D_p as a parameter, and
Figure 12.3b shows experimentally measured values obtained on n-type

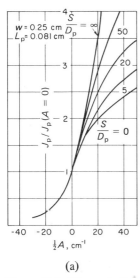

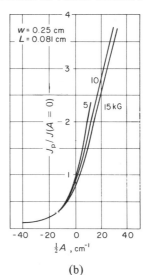

(a)   (b)

Figure 12.3. Theoretically calculated and experimental measurements of normalized
current densities as a function of the parameter $\frac{1}{2}A$ [Equation (12.8)] for single-
junction Hall transducer: (a) calculated values and (b) experimentally measured data
on bulk n-type Ge (after Milnes and Weber [226]).

(5 to 15 ohm cm) germanium. The experimental and theoretical characteristics agree quite well for negative and small positive values of $\frac{1}{2}A$. For high values of $\frac{1}{2}A$ the experimentally measured current density does not tend towards saturation unless unreasonably large surface recombination velocities are assumed within the framework of this first-order theory. Furthermore, the relation $J_p(A)$ is not independent of the magnetic induction, as suggested by the theoretically derived curve. More realistic assumptions in regard to the charge-carrier distribution in and about the junction would be required to bring the theoretically derived data in line with experimental measurements.

A two-junction Hall generator, such as shown in Figure 12.1b, was described by Longini [227]. The semiconductor body is n-doped Ge and both junctions are reverse-biased. A magnetic field applied normal to the plate causes an increase in the flow of minority carriers towards one of the junctions. This Hall current is proportional to the magnetic induction and to the input current i_s. The output voltage across the load resistance is essentially independent of the internal resistance of the Hall generator.

The effect of a transverse magnetic field on the switching properties of a reverse-biased double-base diode was described by Siebertz et al. [228]. Either monostable or bistable switching can be produced by the Hall field, depending on the load line and the transfer characteristic of the device.

Back-biased p–n junction diodes or transistors have been proposed [229] for use as magnetic-tape playback transducers. The recorded magnetic induction increases the minority carrier flow across the narrow depletion region of silicon junction devices, and a further advantage claimed for such transducers is their high resistance to mechanical abrasions due to wear from the magnetic tape. A different magnetic-tape playback transducer was suggested by Stein [230]. It is shown schematically in Figure 12.4. A substrate of high-resistivity p-type InAs has a thin n-type layer diffused or grown upon it, forming a p–n junction. The input current is applied in a direction which is parallel to the junction, and the Hall voltage output is derived in a direction which is transverse to the longitudinal magnetization in the tape and the direction of the current. A p–n junction normal to the direction of the Hall generator plane can be used to control its effective thickness and consequently its sensitivity, as shown by Janicki and Kobus [231]. An n-type Si layer diffused into a p-type substrate constitutes the p–n junction. Input current and Hall electrodes are attached to this layer. A potential is applied to the junction, causing it to be reverse-biased, and this potential controls the thickness of Hall generator. The Hall voltage is

$$v_h = R_h \frac{i_1 B}{d_0 - d_1} G\left(\frac{l}{w}, \frac{s}{w}, \phi\right) , \tag{12.13}$$

where $G(l/w, s/w, \phi)$ is a geometry-dependent function described in Section 3.2, d_0 is the thickness defined by the location of the (metallurgical) p–n junction, and d_1 is the effective thickness determined by the potential applied to the p–n junction. A fair approximation is

$$\frac{\Delta v_h(B)}{\Delta v_h(B = 0)} \approx \frac{d_0}{d_0 - d_1} \,. \tag{12.14}$$

A number of problems must be overcome if practical use is to be made of such Hall generators. These include: (1) the depolarization of the junction due to the voltage drop along the layer produced by the Hall input current; (2) a reverse current flows across the junction; (3) a mobility thickness gradient is present in the layer.

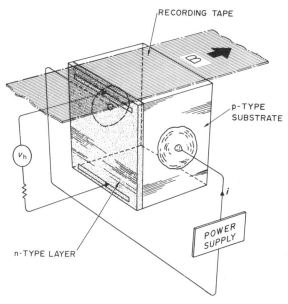

Figure 12.4. Magnetic tape playback transducer uses isolation of n layer (due to p–n junction) from bulk p-type crystal; Hall electrodes are on n layer, and magnetic induction of tape is perpendicular to input current and Hall output signal (after Stein [230]).

12.2 Integrated circuits
Hall generators and magnetoresistors can be integrated on a monolithic silicon chip with active circuit elements, such as transistors and passive networks, or components, such as diodes, resistors, and capacitors. Amplification of the low-level Hall output voltages, isolation of the output from the input circuits, and compensation of thermal and other perturbations can be built into the unitary Hall generator transducer.

Figure 12.5 shows the structure of an integral metal-oxide-semiconductor (MOS) silicon transistor and a Hall generator. If a negative voltage is applied between the gate and source electrodes, then the n-type silicon surface between the source and drain is converted to p-type conduction. A hole current flows between drain and source in the inversion layer, whose dimensions are, typically, $l \approx 0 \cdot 25$ cm, $w \approx 0 \cdot 05$ cm, and $d \leqslant 1$ μm. Gallagher and Corak [232] found that the Hall voltage produced by the application of a magnetic induction in a direction transverse to the inversion layer is a linear function of the drain current. However, the Hall voltage does depend on the source–drain voltage and on the gate voltage. The saturation of the drain current with source–drain voltage produces a saturation of the Hall output voltage. For a gate voltage of -45 V and a drain current of 1 mA, the sensitivity $\gamma_B = 10$ mV kG^{-1} for a p-channel MOS transistor, with a depletion layer having an $l/w \approx 3$. Conflicting geometrical form factor requirements for the transistor and for the Hall generator, respectively, must be reconciled in the design of such integrated circuits. For a high transconductance, typically 1500 μmho, an MOS transistor requires very small l/w ratios, typically of the order of 0·05. On the other hand, an l/w ratio, such as needed for Hall generator applications, typically $l/w \approx 3$, reduces the transconductance of the transistor to $\sim$100 μmho. Integrated Hall generator–MOS configurations with higher γ_B values can be produced by means of n-type inversion layers on Si or on III–V compound semiconductors such as GaAs.

Integrated Hall generators are also compatible with dipolar transistors, as shown by Bosch [233]. Such integrated circuits were produced by photolithographic techniques and by p–n diffusion procedures on $\sim$10 μm thick epitaxially-grown Si layers. A typical Hall generator

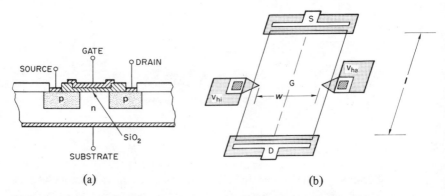

(a)   (b)

Figure 12.5. Integrated circuit transistor–Hall generator: (a) structure of MOS transistor; (b) region of inversion layer in which Hall voltage is generated; v_{hi} and v_{ha} are Hall electrodes, G is superposed gate electrode, l and w are the effective length and width of Hall generators (after Gallagher, R. C., Corak, W. S., 1966, *Solid-State Electron.*, **9**, 337).

sensitivity $\gamma_B = 60$ mV kG^{-1} for an input current of 10 mA and an $l/w = 2$. The Hall generator output terminals are connected to a balanced audio amplifier on the same substrate. The total noise voltage in the audio-frequency range ($f < 15$ kHz) was found to be $0 \cdot 4$ μV.

Silicon Hall generators have an order-of-amplitude smaller sensitivity γ_B than comparable InSb or InAs devices. However, amplifiers integrated on the same silicon chip as Hall generators can boost the Hall output signal. Also, close-spacing between the Hall sensor and the integrated circuit amplifier minimizes noise pickup on the signal leads and improves the thermal stability of the circuit. An integrated circuit noncontacting mechanical switch for a computer terminal keyboard was developed by the Microswitch Divison of the Honeywell Corp. [234]. A Hall generator and switching circuits are integrated on the same silicon chip. A U-shaped magnetic circuit with two permanent magnets provides a transverse magnetic induction of ~$0 \cdot 75$ kG and is attached to the key plunger. A $0 \cdot 5$ cm displacement of the plunger, produced by pushing the key button, carries the magnets over the circuit and generates a 10 mV output signal in the Hall generator. This is fed to the switching amplifiers shown in Figure 12.6. Transistors Q_1 and Q_2 operate as a Schmitt trigger to deliver a IV signal to transistor Q_3, which is a pnp device whose collector load resistance is part of the Hall generator circuit.

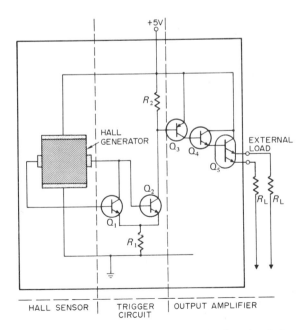

Figure 12.6. Silicon integrated circuit keyboard switch employing a Hall generator and trigger amplifiers on same chip (after [234]).

Transistors Q_4 and Q_5 form a Darlington output driver, and the dual emitters on Q_5 avoid the requirement of two separate output transistors. A 5 V power supply with a 15 mA quiescent current is employed to provide two 10 mA, 3·5 V output signals. The device exhibits hysteresis between the 'on' and 'off' positions of the plunger. This is a desirable feature because it avoids multiple signals which result from 'contact bounce' of mechanical switches and relays.

An integrated circuit function generator, made of photolithographically-processed 6 μm thick InSb attached to a 100 μm thick glass substrate, was produced by Denki Onkyo [235]. It consists of two Hall generators at right angles to each other. One is fed by a constant current power supply and generates, in a transverse magnetic induction, a Hall voltage which provides the source of current for the second Hall generator. Since it too is subjected to the same magnetic induction, its output voltage is proportional to B^2. The precision of such an integrated squaring function generator is reported to be ~0·2% for $B < 3$ kG. Hall generator transistor integrated circuits, with sensitivities of 0·2 mV G^{-1} and transistor beta values from 2 to 4, have also been reported recently [236]; large-scale integrated circuits employing Hall generators for nondestructive readout of recorded digital information on thin-film magnetic memory arrays have also been proposed [237, 238], but no practical implementation of these technologically-feasible proposals has been carried out.

References

1 Smith, R. A., 1959, *Semiconductors* (Cambridge University Press, Cambridge), p.97.
2 Hulme, K. F., Mullin, J. B., 1962, *Solid-State Electron.,* **5**, 211.
3 Liang, S. C., 1962, in *Compound Semiconductors,* volume 1, Eds. R. K. Willardson, H. L. Goering (Reinhold, New York), p.227.
4 Madelung, O., Weiss, H., 1954, *Z. Naturf.,* **9a**, 527.
5 Hrostowski, H. J., Morin, F. J., Geballe, T. H., Wheatley, G. H., 1955, *Phys. Rev.,* **100**, 1672.
6 Guenther, K. G., Freller, H., 1961, *Z. Naturf.,* **16a**, 279.
7 Koike, R., Ueda, R., 1964, *Jap. J. Appl. Phys.,* **3**, 191.
8 Williamson, W. J., 1966, *Solid-State Electron.,* **9**, 213.
9 Wieder, H. H., 1965, *Solid State Commun.,* **3**, 159.
10 Davis, N M , 1967, *Record IEEE 9th Ann. Symp. Electron, Ion and Laser Beam Technology, Berkeley* (San Francisco Press, San Francisco).
11 Teede, N. F., 1967, *Solid-State Electron.,* **10**, 1069.
12 Schroeder, J. B., 1962, in *Compound Semiconductors,* volume 1, Eds. R. K. Willardson, H. L. Goering (Reinhold, New York), p.222.
13 Folberth, O. G., Madelung, O., Weiss, H., 1954, *Z. Naturf.,* **9a**, 954.
14 Hilsum, C., 1960, *Solid State Phys. Electron. Commun.,* **2**, 733.
15 Cronin, C. R., Conrad, W., Borello, S. R., 1966, *J. Electrochem. Soc.,* **113**, 1336.
16 McCarthy, J. P., 1967, *Solid-State Electron.,* **10**, 649.
17 Weiss, H., 1956, *Z. Naturf.,* **11a**, 430.
18 Folberth, O. G., 1955, *Z, Naturf.,* **10a**, 502.
19 Wieder, H. H., Clawson, A. R., 1964, *Proc. Int. Conf. Physics of Semiconductors* (Dunod, Paris), p.1155.
20 Wieder, H. H., Collins, D. A., 1966, *Appl. Phys. Lett.,* **8**, 239.
21 Davis, N. M., Wieder, H. H., 1966, *Proc. 8th Ann. Electron and Laser Beam Symp.* (University of Michigan Press, Ann Arbor), p.385.
22 Weiss, H., Wilhelm, M., 1963, *Z. Phys.,* **176**, 399.
23 Mueller, A., Wilhelm, M., 1967, *Mat. Res. Bull.,* **2**, 531.
24 Putley, E. H., 1960, *The Hall Effect and Related Phenomena* (Butterworths, London), pp.86, 180.
25 Onsager, L., 1931, *Phys. Rev.,* **38**, 2265.
26 Casimir, H. B. G., 1946, *Philips Res. Rept.,* **1**, 185.
27 Chambers, R. G., 1952, *Proc. Phys. Soc.,* A, **65**, 903.
28 Hilsum, C., Rose-Innes, A. C., 1961, *Semiconducting III–V Compounds* (Pergamon Press, New York, London), p.149.
29 Hilsum, C., Barrie, R., 1958, *Proc. Phys. Soc.,* **71**, 675.
30 Weiss, H., 1969, *Structure and Application of Galvanomagnetic Devices* (Pergamon Press, New York, London), p.44.
31 Wick, R. F., 1954, *J. Appl. Phys.,* **25**, 741.
32 Lippmann, H. J., Kuhrt, F., 1958, *Z. Naturf.,* **13a**, 462.
33 Haeusler, J., 1962, *Z. Naturf.,* **17a**, 506.
34 Haeusler, J., 1966, *Solid-State Electron.,* **9**, 417.
35 Newsome, J. P., 1963, *Proc. IEE,* **110**, 653.
36 Gruetzmann, S., 1966, *Solid-State Electron.,* **9**, 409.
37 Newsome, J. P., 1967, *Solid-State Electron.,* **10**, 183.
38 Knotek, M. L., White, D. J., 1966, "The application of difference equations and computer matrix inversion techniques to rectangular Hall plates", NWC Corona Lab's, Corona, California, Tech. Memo C612-1.
39 Haeusler, J., 1968, *Arch. Elektrotech.,* **52**, 11.
40 Isenberg, I., Russel, B. R., Greene, R. F., 1948, *Rev. Sci. Instrum.,* **19**, 685.

41 Volger, J., 1950, *Phys. Rev.*, **79**, 1023.
42 Weiss, H., Welker, H., 1954, *Z. Phys.*, **138**, 122.
43 Binns, K. J., Lawrenson, P. J., 1963, *Analysis and Computation of Electric and Magnetic Field Problems* (Pergamon Press, Oxford), p.158.
44 Kuhrt, F., 1954, *Siemens, Z.*, **28**, 370.
45 Endsley, D. L., Grannemann, W. W., Rosier, L. L., 1961, *IRE Trans. Electron. Devices*, **ED-8**, 220.
46 Datta, S. K., Daw, A. N., 1964, *Z. Naturf.*, **19a**, 392.
47 Datta, S. K., Daw, A. N., 1967, *Solid-State Electron.*, **10**, 733.
48 Haeusler, J., Lippmann, H. J., 1968, *Solid-State Electron.*, **11**, 173.
49 Halla, O., 1967, US Patent No. 3 348 184, 17 October 1967 (filed 24 October 1965).
50 Kuhrt, F., Hartel, W., 1957, *Archiv. Elektrotech.*, **43**, 1.
51 Wood, C., Tischler, O., Schroeder, G. F., 1961, *Rev. Sci., Instrum.*, **32**, 209.
52 Roth, H., Straub, W. D., 1962, *J. Appl. Phys.*, **33**, 2397.
53 Daw, A. N., Majumdar, N. C., 1964, *Z. Naturf.*, **19a**, 1630.
54 Fraenkel, D., Gruen, V., 1969, *Solid-State Electron.*, **12**, 201.
55 Shirer, D. L., 1960, *Rev. Sci. Instrum.*, **31**, 1000
56 Wieder, H. H., 1962, *Rev. Sci. Instrum.*, **33**, 64
57 Sun, S. F., 1963, *Proc. IEEE*, **51**, 1255.
58 Weiss, H., 1966, US Patent 3 260 980, 12 July 1966 (filed 12 March 1963).
59 Rubin, S., Epstein, M., Katz, H., Stevens, R., 1969, *IEEE Standard Definitions of Terms on Hall Effect Devices*, number 296, May.
60 Serkov, V. V., 1962, *Avtomatika i Telemekhanika*, **23**, 383.
61 Von der Ziel, A., 1959, *Fluctuation Phenomena in Semiconductors* (Academic Press, London), p.48.
62 Burckhardt, C. B., Strutt, M. J. O., 1964, *IEEE Trans. Electron. Devices*, **ED-11**, 47.
63 Oliver, D. J., 1957, *Proc. Phys. Soc.* B, **70**, 331.
64 Epstein, M., 1965, *J. Appl. Phys.*, **63**, 2590.
65 Brophy, J. J., 1958, *Phys. Rev.*, **111**, 1050.
66 Chasmar, R. P., Cohen, E., Holmes, D. P., 1959, *Proc. IEE*, **106B**, supplement 16, 705.
67 Glinski, G. S., Landolt, J. P., 1961, *Conv. Rec. IRE*, **9**, 143.
68 Weiss, H., 1969, *Structure and Application of Galvanomagnetic Devices* (Pergamon Press, Oxford), p.108.
69 Halpern, L., Koch, K. M., 1951, *Acta Phys. Austria*, **5**, 129.
70 Campbell, L. L., 1923, *Galvanomagnetic and Thermomagnetic Effects* (Longmans, Green, New York), pp.159–170.
71 Welker, H., Weiss, H., 1961, US Patent 2 989 715, 20 June 1961.
72 Kallman, H. E., 1963, US Patent 3 109 985, 5 November 1963.
73 Weiss, H., Welker, H., 1954, *Z. Phys.*, **138**, 322.
74 Welker, H., 1955, *Elektrotech. Z.*, **76**, 513.
75 Weiss, H., Welker, H., 1959, US Patent 2 894 234, 7 July 1959.
76 Wieder, H. H., Collins, D. A., 1968, *Solid-State Electron.*, **11**, 1093.
77 Weiss, H., 1966, *Solid-State Electron.*, **9**, 443.
78 Weiss, H., 1965, *Elektrotech. Z.*, **17**, 289.
79 Kapitza, P., 1928, *Proc. R. Soc.* A, **119**, 401.
80 Thompson, N., 1936, *Proc. R. Soc.* A, **135**, 111.
81 Hunt, J. M., 1960, Tech. Rep. 1504-1, Solid-State Electronics Laboratories, Stanford University, Stanford, California.
82 Shiffman, C. A., 1962, *Rev. Sci. Instrum.*, **33**, 206.
83 Germain, C., 1963, *Nuclear Instrum. Methods*, **21**, 17.

84 Weiss, H., 1960, *Solid-State Electron.*, **1**, 225.
85 Mulady, J. R., 1964, *IEEE Trans. Instrum. Meas.*, **IM-13**, 343.
86 Collins, J. R., 1963, *Electron. Wld.*, **69**, 39.
87 Ross, I. M., Saker, E. W., Thompson, N. A. C., 1957, *J. Sci. Instrum.*, **34**, 479.
88 Hieronymus, H., Weiss, H., 1957, *Siemens Z.*, **31**, 404.
89 Warmuth, K., 1954, *Arch. Elektrotech.*, **41**, 242.
90 Epstein, M., Schulz, R. B., 1961, *IRE Trans. Electron. Devices*, **ED-8**, 70.
91 Owston, C. N., 1967, *J. Sci. Instrum.*, **44**, 798.
92 Milligan, N. P., Burgess, J. P., 1964, *Solid-State Electron.*, **7**, 323.
93 Keller, E. A., 1962, *Proc. Natn. Electron. Conf.*, volume 18 (National Electronics Conference Inc., Chicago), p.753.
94 Epstein, M., Van Scoyoc, J. N., Greenstein, L. J., 1961, *Proc. Natn. Electron. Conf.*, volume 17 (National Electronics Conference Inc., Chicago), p.611.
95 von Borcke, U., Martens, H., Weiss, H., 1965, *Solid-State Electron.*, **8**, 365.
96 Craik, D. J., 1968, *J. Sci. Instrum.*, [2], **1**, 1193.
97 Viehmann, W., 1962, *Rev. Sci. Instrum.*, **33**, 537.
98 Berkowitz, D. A., Schippert, M. A., 1966, *J. Sci. Instrum.*, **43**, 56.
99 Hennig, G. R., 1958, *Elect. Mfg.*, **61**, 132.
100 Roshon, D. D. Jr., 1962, *Rev. Sci. Instrum.*, **33**, 201.
101 Assmus, F., Boll, R., 1956, *Elektrotech. Z.*, **A77**, 234.
102 Kostyshyn, B., Roshon, D. D. Jr., 1959, *Proc. IRE*, **47**, 451.
103 Kuhrt, F., Hartel, W., 1956, *Arch. Elektrotech.*, **42**, 398.
104 Wieder, H. H., 1962, *J. Appl. Phys.*, **33**, 1278.
105 Wieder, H. H., 1962, *Rev. Sci. Instrum.*, **33**, 64.
106 Hilsum, C., Rose-Innes, A. C., 1958, *Nature, Lond.*, **182**, 1082.
107 Ross, L. M., Saker, E. W., 1955, *J. Electron.*, **2**, 223.
108 Whitlock, W. H., Hilsum, C., 1960, *Nature, Lond.*, **185**, 302.
109 Maaz, K., Schmid, R., 1957, *Elektrotech. Z.*, **A78**, 734.
110 Serkov, V. V., 1962, *Pribory i Tekh. Eksp.*, **1**, 124 (transl. *Instrum. and Exp. Tech.*, **1**, 125 (1962)].
111 Löfgren, L., 1955, *Proc. Int. Ann. Comp. Meeting, Brussels* (Presses Academiques Europ., Brussels), p.111.
112. Löfgren, L., 1958, *J. Appl. Phys.*, **29**, 158.
113 Chasmar, R. P., Cohen, E., Holmes, D. P., 1959, *Proc. Instn. Elect. Engrs.*, **106B**, 16.
114 Greiner, R. A., 1961, *Electronics*, **34**, 52.
115 Cohen, E., 1962, *Electron. Engng.*, **34**, 316.
116 Hartel, W., 1954, *Siemens Z.*, **28**, 376.
117 Saraga, W., Galpin, R. K. P., 1964, *Solid-State Electron.*, **7**, 335.
118 Claudin, P., Fric, C., 1964, *C. R. Acad. Sci., Paris*, **259**, 1307.
119 Kovatch, G., Meserve, W. E., 1961, *IRE Trans. Electron. Comp.*, **EC-10**, 512.
120 Sun, S. F., 1964, *Electronics*, **37**, 66.
121 Sun, S. F., 1964, *Solid-State Electron.*, **7**, 363.
122 Wieder, H. H., 1965, *Electronics*, **38**, 120.
123 Gitlin, R. M., 1965, *Electromech. Des.*, **9**, 58.
124 Gitlin, R. M., 1967, *Analogue–Dialogue*, **1**, 1.
125 Wieder, H. H., 1963, *Rev. Sci. Instrum.*, **34**, 422.
126 Wieder, H. H., 1963, *Electronics*, **36**, 46.
127 Hutcheon, I. C., 1966, *Electron. Lett.*, **2**, 462.
128 Hutcheon, I. C., Harrison, D. N., 1965, *Instrum. Pract.*, **19**, 529.
129 Miteva, V. I., Vichev, B. I., 1966, *Electron. Lett.*, **2**, 364.
130 Wieder, H. H., 1964, *Electronics*, **37**, 30.
131 Miteva, V. I., Vichev, B. I., 1967, *Electron. Lett.*, **3**, 22.

132 Ohno, I., Ohta, S., 1963, *Elect. Engng., Japan,* **83**, 27
133 Billings, A. R., 1962, *Proc. IRE (Australia),* **23**, 412.
134 Billings, A. R., Lloyd, D. J., 1959, *Proc. IEE,* **106B**, supplement 16, 706.
135 Kataoka, S., Yamada, H., 1962, *Proc. IRE,* **50**, 2522.
136 Barlow, H. E. M., 1955, *Proc. IEE,* **102B**, 186.
137 Strutt, M. J. O., Sun, S. F., 1955, *Arch. Elektrotech.,* **42**, 155.
138 Strutt, M. J. O., 1958, *Scientia Electrica,* **4**, 92.
139 Strutt, M. J. O., 1959, *Electron. Radio Engng.,* **36**, 2.
140 Kanellakos, D. P., Schuk, R. P., Todd, A. C., 1961, *IRE Trans. Audio,* **9**, 5.
141 Crawford, R. W., 1966, *Solid-State Electron.,* **9**, 527.
142 Barlow, H. E. M., Kataoka, S., 1958, *Proc. IEE,* **105B**, 53.
143 Rugari, A. D., 1962, *Electron. Ind.,* **21**, J6.
144 Barlow, H. E. M., Stephenson, L. M., 1956, *Proc. IEE,* **103B**, 110.
145 Stephenson, L. M., Barlow, H. E. M., 1959, *Proc. IEE,* **106B**, 27.
146 Strutt, M. J. O., Sun, S. F., 1961, *IRE Trans. Instrum.,* **I-10**, 44.
147 Kataoka, S., 1962, *Proc. IRE,* **50**, 216.
148 Kataoka, S., 1964, *Proc. IEE,* **111**, 1937.
149 Kataoka, S., 1963, *Proc. IEEE,* **51**, 380.
150 Kataoka, S., Naito, H., 1966, *Solid-State Electron.,* **9**, 459.
151 Rehm, G., 1960, *Arch. Tech. Mess.,* **J86-5**, 61.
152 Epstein, M., Greenstein, L. J., 1962, *IRE Int. Conv. Rec.,* **9**, 186.
153 Kuhrt, F., Braunersreuther, E., 1954, *Siemens Z.,* **28**, 299.
154 Loocke, G., 1955, *Elektrotech. Z.,* **A76**, 517.
155 Elpat'evskaia, O. D., Matus, I. A., Perchuk, V. A., 1958, *Sov. Phys.-Tech. Phys.,*
     3, 1854.
156 Menzel, P., 1961, *Arch. Tech. Mess.,* **V-392-2**, 83.
157 Koehler, W., 1961, *Arch. Tech. Mess.,* **V-8251-5**, 131.
158 Hollitscher, H., 1966, *Solid-State Electron.,* **9**, 581.
159 Nalecz, M., 1961, *Bull. Acad. Pol. Sci.,* **9**, 469.
160 Nalecz, M., 1961, *Electron. Tech.,* **38**, 15.
161 Shull, F. B., MacFarland, C. E., Bretscher, M. M., 1954, *Rev. Sci. Instrum.,* **25**,
     364.
162 Jagger, J. W., Riley, P. J., 1967, *Rev. Sci. Instrum.,* **7**, 955.
163 Nalecz, M., Warsza, Z. L., 1966, *Solid-State Electron.,* **9**, 485.
164 Nalecz, M., Zawicki, I., 1962, *Bull. Seism. Soc. Am.,* **52**, 439.
165 Nalecz, M., Ziomecki, H., 1963, *J. Franklin Inst.,* **276**, 14.
166 Ross, I. M., Saker, E. W., 1955, *Nature, Lond.,* **175**, 518.
167 Yuan, L. T., 1966, *Solid-State Electron.,* **9**, 497,
168 Williamson, W. J., 1968, *IEEE Trans. Mag.,* **MAG-1**, 162.
169 Fay, L. E., 1959, *Control Engng.,* **6**, 131.
170 Harac, S., Tischler, O., 1961, *Electromech. Des.,* **5**, 14.
171 Ratajski, Z. R. S., 1961, *Electronics,* **34**, 59.
172 Donaldson, G. W., 1963, *Electron. Engng.,* **35**, 286.
173 Parsons, T. W., Simon, T. R., 1962, *IRE Conv. Rec.,* **6**, 169.
174 Grancoin B., 1967, US Patent 3 309 642, issued 14 March 1967.
175 Davidson, R. S., Gourlay, R. D., 1966, *Solid-State Electron.,* **9**, 471.
176 Inglis, B. D., Donaldson, G. W., 1966, *Solid-State Electron.,* **9**, 541.
177 Strandt, E. R., 1963, *IEEE Trans. Instrum. Meas.,* **IM-12**, 22.
178 Weiss, H., Hini, P., 1967, US Patent 3 331 045, issued 11 July 1967.
179 Weiss, H., 1967, US Patent 3 335 384, issued 8 August 1967.
180 Weiss, H., Hini, P., 1968, US Patent 3 366 908, issued 30 January 1968.
181 Albrecht, A., Hini, P., 1967, US Patent 3 359 522, issued 19 December 1967.
182 Wilson, T. G., Trickey, P. H., 1962, *Electr. Engng.,* **81**, 879.

183 Bauerlein, G., 1962, *IRE Conv. Rec.,* **6**, 184.
184 Kuhrt, F., 1966, *Solid-State Electron.,* **9**, 567.
185 Dittrich, W., Rainer, E., 1966, *Siemens Z.,* **40**, 690.
186 Quichaud, G., Bonnefille, R., 1965, *J. Phys. Appl.,* **26**, 22A.
187 Hini, P., Weiss, H., 1968, US Patent 3366909, issued 30 January 1968.
188 Berman, L. S., Raikhman, S. S., Khalfin, Z. A., 1957, *Sov. Phys.-Tech. Phys.,* **2**, 1480.
189 Bogomolov, V. N., Vasil'ev, V. D., 1957, *Sov. Phys.-Tech. Phys.,* **2**, 229.
190 Bogomolov, V. N., Myasnikov, V. A., 1959, *Auto. Rem. Control,* **20**, 774.
191 Cohen, E., 1962, *Electron. Engng.,* **34**, 316.
192 Keister, G. L., 1956, *Control Engng.,* **2**, 94.
193 Hilhinger, A. R., 1964, *Electronics,* **37**, 30.
194 Epstein, M., Greenstein, L. J., Sachs, H. M., 1959, *Proc. Natn. Electron. Conf.,* volume 15 (National Electronics Conference Inc., Chicago), p.1.
195 Epstein, M., Brophy, J. J., 1966, *Solid-State Electron.,* **9**, 507.
196 Hess, J. J. Jr., 1960, US Patent 2941163, issued 14 June 1960.
197 Barlow, H. E. M., Krishna, K. V. G., 1962, *Proc. IEE,* **109B**, 131.
198 Chang, K. K. N., Hughes, R. D., 1963, *J. Appl. Phys.,* **34**, 777.
199 Chasmar, R. P., Openshaw, B., 1962, *Electron. Engng.,* **34**, 755.
200 Weisshaar, E., 1959, US Patent 2902660, issued 1 September 1959.
201 Hieronymus, H., Weiss, H., 1963, *Solid-State Electron.,* **6**, 463.
202 Bechtel, R., Grannemann, W. W., Harper, B. J., 1964, *Solid-State Electron.,* **7**, 357.
203 Wieder, H. H., 1969, US Patent 3435323, issued 25 March 1969.
204 Billings, A. R., Lloyd, D. J., 1960, *Proc. IEE,* **107B**, 435.
205 Holler, E., Wolf, D., 1965, *Z. Angew. Phys.,* **19**, 364.
206 Brophy, J. J., Epstein, M., Webb, S. L., 1965, *Rev. Sci. Instrum.,* **36**, 1803.
207 Billings, A. R., Forward, K. E., 1965, *Proc. IEE,* **112**, 689.
208 Williams, J. D., Denker, S. P., 1960, "A Fourier analyzer employing Hall effect multiplication", Tech. Rep. 157, MIT Lab. for Insul. Res.
209 Williams, J. D., Denker, S. P. 1961, *Electron. Ind.,* **20**, 108.
210 Greenstein, L. J., Shaifer, T. R., Epstein, M., 1964, *Rev. Sci. Instrum.,* **35**, 1307.
211 Anderson, P. R., Collins, C. R., 1965, *Electron. Des.,* **13**, 22.
212 Smerage, G. H., 1964, *Int. Solid-State Circ. Conf.,* volume SES 11 (Lewis Winner, New York), p.94.
213 Mee, C. D., *The Physics of Magnetic Recording* (Interscience, John Wiley, New York).
214 Camras, M., 1962, *Proc. IRE,* **50**, 751.
215 Camras, M., 1955, *IRE Trans. Audio,* **AU-3**, 174.
216 Kornei, O., 1955, *J. Acoust. Soc. Am.,* **27**, 575.
217 Kuhrt, F., Stark, G., Wolf, F., 1959, *Elektron. Rdsch.,* **11**, 407.
218 Camras, M., 1962, *IRE Trans. Audio,* **AU-10**, 84.
219 Kuhrt, F., Stark, G., 1964, US Patent 3146317, issued 25 August 1964.
220 Kuhrt, F., Stark, G., 1964, US Patent 3163721, issued 29 December 1964.
221 Neumann, H., 1965, US Patent 3209078, issued 28 September 1965.
222 Howling, D. H., 1961, US Patent 2978545, issued 4 April 1961.
223 Stein, I., 1961, Wescon Convention Record 13/3.
224 Koehler, H., Kostyshyn, B., Ku, T. C., 1961, *IBM J. Res. Dev.,* **5**, 326.
225 Suhl, H., 1949, *Phys. Rev.,* **75**, 1617.
226 Milnes, A. G., Weber, E. V., 1959, *Proc. Electron. Comp. Conf., Philadelphia, Pa.,* 6-8 May 1959, p.204.
227 Longini, R. L., 1958, US Patent 2862184, issued 25 November 1958.

228 Siebertz, K., Henker, H., Dorendorf, H., 1962, US Patent 3035183, issued 15 May 1962.
229 Hyland, J. F., 1968, US Patent 3373247, issued 12 March 1968.
230 Stein, I., 1965, US Patent 3202770, issued 24 August 1965.
231 Janicki, T., Kobus, A., 1967, *Electron. Lett.*, **3**, 373.
232 Gallagher, R. C., Corak, W. S., 1966, *Solid-State Electron.*, **9**, 571.
233 Bosch, G., 1968, *Solid-State Electron.*, **11**, 712.
234 Microswitch Div., Honeywell Corp., Freeport, Ill., 1969, "Solid state switch", Product Sheet 1SS1.
235 Denki Onkyo, 1969, *Electronics*, **42**, 254.
236 McDermott, J., 1969, *Electron. Des.*, **17**, 38.
237 Cushman, R. H., 1968, *Electron. Des. News*, **13**, 87.
238 Maass, J. A., 1969, US Patent 3443036, issued 6 May 1969.
239 McMillan, E. M., 1946, *J. Acoust. Soc. Am.*, **18**, 344.
240 McMillan, E. M., 1947, *J. Acoust. Soc. Am.*, **19**, 922.
241 Tellegen, B. D. H., 1948, *Philips Res. Rep.*, **3**, 81.
242 Kataoka, S., Hashizume, N., 1965, *Proc. IEEE*, **53**, 2138.
243 Toda, M., 1966, *Proc. IEEE*, **54**, 1456.
244 Gruetzmann, S., 1963, *Proc. IEEE*, **51**, 1584.
245 Renton, C. A., 1965, *Proc. IEEE*, **53**, 755.
246 Mason, W. P., Hewitt, W. H., Wick, R. F., 1953, *J. Appl. Phys.*, **24**, 166.
247 Wick, R. F., 1954, *J. Appl. Phys.*, **25**, 741.
248 Grubbs, W. J., 1959, *Bell Syst. Tech. J.*, **38**, 853.
249 Kobus, A., 1968, *Solid-State Electron.*, **11**, 903.
250 Shockley, W., Mason, W. P., 1954, *J. Appl. Phys.*, **25**, 677.
251 Grubbs, W. J., 1961, *IRE Trans. Electron. Devices*, **ED-8**, 163.
252 Kroemer, H., 1964, *Solid-State Electron.*, **7**, 291.
253 Hubbard, R. C., LoSasso, L. A., Ronsso, E., 1961, *Electronics*, **34**, 56.
254 Arlt, G., 1960, *Solid-State Electron.*, **1**, 75.
255 Semmelman, C. L., 1956, US Patent 2774890, issued 18 December 1956.
256 Grubbs, W. J., 1959, *Proc. IRE*, **47**, 528.
257 Silverman, D., 1963, *Electro-Technology*, **71**, 113.
258 Balanov, A. T., Krasilich, G. P., Seleznev, I. I., 1968, *Meas. Tech.*, **2**, 207.
259 Gruetzmann, S., 1964, *Frequenz*, **18**, 42.
260 Gruetzmann, S., 1964, *Frequenz*, **18**, 265.
261 Rubin, S., 1966, *Solid-State Electron.*, **9**, 559.
262 Rubin, S., Rogers, G. J., 1964, Natn. Bur. Stand. Tech. Note 233.
263 Epstein, M., Brophy, J. J., 1965, *IEEE Trans. Electron. Devices*, **ED-12**, 25.
264 Kataoka, S., Hashizume, N., Iida, S., 1968, *Solid-State Electron.*, **11**, 155.

Author Index

Subject Index